ENGINEERING MANAGEMENT

Civil engineering contracts

An introduction to construction contracts and the ICE model form of contract

Stephen Wearne, BSc(Eng), DIC, PhD, CEng, FBIM, FICE

┓╹┓ Thomas Telford, London

Published by Thomas Telford Ltd, Thomas Telford House,
1 Heron Quay, London E14 9XF

First published 1989

British Library Cataloguing in Publicaton Data
Civil engineering contracts: an introduction to construction
  contracts and the ICE model form of contract
  1. Great Britain. Civil engineering.
  Contracts — Manuals
  I. Institution of Civil Engineers
  624

ISBN: 0 7277 1353 1

Typeset in Great Britain by MHL Typesetting Limited
Printed and bound in Great Britain by Billings & Sons Limited, Worcester

To E J W — party to my
successful contract

Preface

- When is an agreement a **contract**?

- What are **conditions** of contract?

- Why are there different **types** of contract and various **terms of payment**, and how do they **motivate** contractors and others?

- What is needed for an **internal** equivalent of a contract between the engineering and the construction departments within an organization?

The answers to these and related questions can have great effects on the success of a project and on the careers and satisfaction of individuals in their work. Engineers therefore need to be able to answer those questions in order to understand and manage relationships with others employed on the planning, design, construction and maintenance of new projects or other work such as renovation. They need increasingly to have good answers to such questions because governments and the private promoters of projects in all countries demand value for money, especially to be more confident that engineers can plan and manage contracts so as to prevent construction from costing more and taking longer than promised.

Experience should provide some knowledge and ideas for answering these demands, but less certainly does it provide sufficient understanding of the legal basis of contractual commitments, rights and obligations or of the potential advantages and disadvantages of alternative types of contract, terms of payment, etc. Experience may include some good lessons, but it can also be too slow, incomplete or misleading. This Guide is intended to help remedy this. It is meant to complement learning on the job, for all engineers whose success in their work depends upon understanding the contract relationships between the **promoters** of projects and the **contractors** who employ people, plant, materials and sub-contractors to construct what has been specified.

Contracts are agreements enforceable by law. They are not unique to business relationships between organizations. They are a basis of many social as well as commercial transactions in Western societies. Paid employment is contractual. So is purchasing a pencil at a shop. And marriage. How we plan and conduct these trans-actions with the other parties to them varies greatly, but all are agreements enforceable by law. The law provides rules for mak-ing contracts so that they will be enforceable. It also provides a system for settling some disputes about contracts.

The law does not prevent bad bargains between companies, public bodies, consultants or others 'in business'. It regards their contracts as private affairs. It expects all such organizations and the individuals in them to know what they are doing when they agree a specification, price, programme or drawing. For a civil engineering project to be a success its promoter and his advisers should therefore first define their objectives and priorities, and then a strategy for managing the risks and uncertainties which may disrupt their intentions. Decisions on contract policy should follow, in particular on who should be responsible for design and con-struction to best suit the size, complexity, novelty, urgency and importance of the new construction or reconstruction required. Contracts and the internal equivalents for ordering construction should be planned and managed as a stage in getting projects com-pleted and in use. They are a means to an end, as indicated in Fig. 1.

Contracts for construction in this and most countries have tradi-tionally been based upon competitive tendering, the promoter (or a consulting engineer on his behalf) issuing drawings, specifica-tions and general instructions to prospective contractors which define in detail what is to be constructed. Employing only one 'main' contractor to undertake all or most of the construction of a project with his own resources plus sub-contractors is also com-mon, but there is great and perhaps increasing variety and some experiment in alternatives to try to get better results. One alter-native is to use several contractors separately on one site. Another alternative to tradition is that a contractor undertakes the responsi-

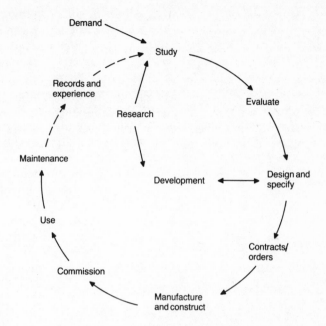

Fig. 1. A contract (or an equivalent internal order between departments within an organization) is a means to an end

bility for most or all the design of a project, as well as its construction, and corresponding to this are promoters who have their own 'in-house' construction departments. In this Guide the traditional procedure is considered, but attention is also given to the alternatives as many civil engineers may need to be able to work in them and be prepared to advise on the choices.

This Guide is therefore in two main parts. The first part is a review of choices in planning a project, particularly the number, type and scope of contracts and contract documents. The second part is an introduction to the use of the model form of contract agreed by the Institution of Civil Engineers and others in Britain. References are also made to one model form agreed for use internationally. Appendices give notes on abbreviations and words used, contracts under English law, latent liabilities, engineers' relationships with auditors, references to further reading, and a list of addresses of organizations.

Most contracts for construction work include a list of definitions of some of the words used in them. This is wise and helpful, but unfortunately the definitions vary from contract to contract and so there are no standard meanings used consistently throughout civil engineering even within the British Isles. As far as possible in this book the most typical meanings are used. The definitions important for an accurate understanding of the chapters are listed in Appendix B. When these defined words are first used in the book they appear in **bold** type.

Acknowledgements

Parts of this Management Guide are based on an internal manual for their staff prepared by Sir William Halcrow & Partners, Consulting Engineers. I gratefully acknowledge this very substantial help.

The responsibility for drafting the final version of the Guide is of course mine, but I am indebted to the authors of their manual, other writers, and former colleagues, bosses, teachers, students and many others for information, comments and advice.

Contents

Appendices

Part I Contract planning

'Caveat emptor' — Buyer be wary

Failures by the promoters of projects to plan contract agreements to suit their objectives and risks are major reasons for **construction** over-running in time and cost. In this and the following chapters the decisions needed in planning to employ contractors are therefore considered.

To be consistent the style of the Institution of Civil Engineers' booklet *Civil Engineering Procedure* in using the word 'promoter' to mean the client or the employer of a contractor is followed.

Many promoters employ a consultant, consulting engineer, lawyers and others for advice, design and other services, and perhaps name one as their **agent**, but in these chapters the word 'promoter' is used alone to mean a promoter and his advisers and representatives. This makes the reading easier. It is also a reminder that they should be a team and speak as one in communications with contractors and any others.

1 Number of contracts

'Two's company, three's a crowd'?

Promoters employ contractors to construct their projects for one or more of the following objectives:

- *A* To utilize the skills and expertise of contractors' managers, engineers, craftsmen, buyers, etc. for the *limited duration* of a project.

- *B* To get contractors to take some of the cost *risks* of a project, usually the risks of planning to use people, plant, materials and sub-contractors economically.

- *C* To get contractors to obtain the *financial* resources for a project, and perhaps also for operating it.

- *D* To be free as promoters to concentrate on the *objectives* of projects, their subsequent use, and other interests.

- *E* To have the benefit of contractors' special *resources* such as licensed processes, unique plant, materials in stock, etc.

- *F* To get work started *quicker* than would be possible by recruiting and training direct employees.

- *G* To encourage the *development* of successful contractors.

One of these objectives may be appropriate to only a part of a project, such as the need to use a licensed process. If so, an option for the promoter is to employ one contractor to construct that part and one or more others for the remainder. Alternatively, a project might be so large that more than one contractor is appropriate to share the risks. A series of contractors could be employed in turn for the demolition, new foundations and then the remainder of the work of replacing a structure, each under different types

3

of contract, particularly if the demolition requires specialist expertise or care to remove dangerous substances. Different contractors could be employed separately for the structural, finishing and services work for a building, instead of one main contractor with these specialist tasks being sub-contracted.

One main contractor

Employing a main contractor has the potential advantage that the one organization is responsible for managing all the people, plant, materials, sub-contracting, etc., and is therefore best for meeting objectives B, C and D listed above.

The potential disadvantages of this are that the whole contract has to be agreed before construction starts, or the contract is made when some of the scope of work or other terms are not finally decided. Terms of contracts used in civil engineering have been evolved to manage the latter problem, but they are complex and are criticized as making it too easy for promoters to postpone or change decisions and for contractors to claim that these have disrupted the basis of their planning and therefore their costs. Also, in this arrangement the promoter has no direct contractual link with or control of sub-contractors employed by the main contractor. Obtaining successful results from using this arrangement can thus depend on the capacity and motivation of the main contractor chosen and on the planning and the management of the contract by or on behalf of its promoter.

Several contractors

The alternative for promoters of dividing a project into several contracts has the potential advantages that contractors can be employed on the categories of work they should do best, as objective A listed, and a start can be made before the scope of all the work for a project has been decided, as objective F. This alternative is more common in other countries. A disadvantage is that the employment of two or more contractors places with the promoter the risks of planning and agreeing a set of contracts and coordinating the design and site relationships between contractors.

● As an example, a port could be constructed under one overall contract, or, at the other extreme, the work could be divided up into separate contracts as follows:

o *Preliminaries*: several separate contracts with local or specialist contractors, e.g. for site investigations, access roads, camp housing, opening of quarry, diversion of public services.

o *Breakwater and quays*: the main contract, with a contractor experienced in marine construction.

o *Dredging*: contract with a specialist contractor.

o *Buildings*: contract with a local building contractor.

o *Roads, drainage, etc*: several contracts with specialist or local contractors.

o *Mechanical and electrical equipment*: contracts with specialist contractors and suppliers who design and supply systems and equipment.

Joint ventures and consortia

Two or more contractors acting together as a **joint venture** or a **consortium** is an arrangement which can meet most of the above objectives *A* to *G*, particularly for large and civil-mechanical-electrical or process engineering projects. In developing countries such joint arrangements are used when a promoter, government or a local contractor wishes the local contractor to gain experience by working with an international contractor.

A joint venture or consortium may include consulting engineers, bankers and others, so as to provide the expertise and resources needed to design, finance, construct and manage a complete project. The potential advantage to the promoter is that the project is the responsibility of one organization, but for this to be effective all the partners in a joint venture or consortium should be committed to the success of the project. Usually this commitment is based upon contracts between them and with the promoter which make each partner liable to the promoter for the performance of the whole contract.

Bibliography

Hayes R.W. et al, *Risk management in engineering construction*, Thomas Telford Ltd, London, 1987. (Gives recommendations on using risk analysis to aid decisions on type of contract, selective or open tendering, and all stages of construction project management).

2 Types of contract

'Horses for courses'

The guiding principle should be to choose a type of contract that is likely to achieve the objectives of a project. The ideal choice therefore varies from project to project, depending upon a promoter's wish for speed, quality, economy, flexibility, experience or other objectives. A limitation on the choice in some countries can be that there are not contractors with the resources and experience required for some types of contract. There may also be national rules which limit what can be negotiated.

The important differences between the possible alternative types of contract for civil engineering projects are in how the risks of design and of construction are shared between promoter and contractor. The agreed wisdom of experienced promoters is that a risk should be the responsibility of whichever **party** is best able to manage it to suit the objectives of a project. All parties to a project are at risk to some extent whatever the contracts between them, for instance that its construction may be frustrated by forces beyond their control. If so, the time lost and all or some of their consequent costs may not be recoverable. What the choice of type of contract can do is motivate (or fail to motivate) those who design and those who construct to be economical, quick or whatever are the priorities for a project.

Traditional construction relationships

In the traditional system evolved in civil engineering in Britain the design of a project is one task of a consulting engineer employed by the promoter, and construction the responsibility of one main contractor selected after tendering in competition with others. In principle, the promoter bears the design risks, except that if the designers are negligent some of his consequent losses may be recoverable. The contractor bears most of the construction risks, except some taken by subcontractors and suppliers of materials, etc.

The process of making a contract therefore begins with the preparation of what are called 'tender documents', in effect the proposed contract **terms**. These ideally include a complete specification and detailed drawings, and are issued to prospective contractors to be the basis of their tenders (offers). The contractors compete by **price**. Quite detailed terms of payment are specified by promoters in the tender documents for some civil engineering contracts, particularly those in Britain based upon bills of quantities as are considered later.

The purpose of competitive tendering is to get contractors to compete in how efficiently they expect to use manpower and their other resources to carry out all that is specified in the tender documents. The expectation is that if all of them are tendering for the same contract, their prices should indicate which contractor will be the most efficient. Some experienced promoters invite tenders only from contractors already selected for having sufficient resources and demonstrated relevant performance. Other promoters make an invitation for tenders **open** to any interested contractor.

The contractor chosen may not be the one who offered the lowest price. Sometimes this is required by law, by a promoter or his financial sources, but others have a contrary policy of not 'buying trouble by buying cheap'. As well as price, these promoters and their advisers may also decide to compare and evaluate differences in resources, past performance, proposed construction methods, construction programmes, subcontractors and differences in the basis of total prices. Some analyse the range of total tender prices statistically and discount ones which appear to be erroneously cheap.

The traditional system has the *potential* advantages to promoters that the competition between the contractors should result in their offering the lowest prices in order to be chosen, and that the price tendered by the chosen contractor is all that the promoter will have to pay. Whether these advantages are gained in practice may depend upon whether a contract includes terms for changes in payments, for changes in the scope or quality of work, **escalation** of primary costs or other reasons, and how those terms are used. The inclusion of such provisions in civil engineering contracts has been criticized. The validity of the criticisms depends in each case on the extent that changes are made after the contract takes effect and whether their results cause failure to achieve the objectives of project and promoter.

A more fundamental basis for criticism of this system is that it separates the responsibilities for design and for construction, and so has the potential disadvantages that either the designers have to make assumptions about how a project will be constructed before the contractor has been chosen and his methods of construction are known, or when construction should be under way design changes may have to be made to take advant ge of the contractor's recommendations. This system also limits the extent that the engineers and others employed in one or other stage of a project can see and learn from the consequences of their work on a project as a whole. That may also affect their motivation at work.

The above criticism may be partly overcome by consultations between design engineers and contractors before tenders are invited in order to incorporate ideas to suit construction. This has to be managed so as not to affect the intentions of policies for competition between the prospective contractors for a contract. Even if there is consultation, the division of engineering expertise in the traditional system may result in sub-optimization of the balance between quality, cost and speed. It is unique to the building and civil engineering industries. Its origin is in the establishment of consulting engineers in the XIXth Century in Britain as advisers and designers in the boom of canal, railway and other construction, and the separate growth of 'labour contractors' into construction companies. The development of this system has possibly continued because promoters wish the design decisions which determine the scope and standard and therefore most of the cost of a project to be separate from the commercial interests of contractors. Many promoters use adaptations of the traditional system, without a consulting engineer having independent authority to give instructions to a contractor that affect costs.

Design-and-construct contracts

One obvious alternative to the traditional system in civil engineering is that a contractor should be responsible for both design and construction. This alternative is variously known as a **design-and-construct, all-in, turnkey** or **package deal** contract, but the meaning of these words is not precise as the scope of the contractors' responsibilities for deciding standards, buying land, obtaining planning permission and choosing suppliers can be different from contract to contract.

This alternative is also known as a **performance** contract, indicating that the contractor takes the risks of designing a project to achieve the performance specified, but again each such contract can be different from others in the extent that the promoter and advisers specify their requirements and in how much they check design and construction.

The potential advantages of this type of contract are the undivided responsibility for design and construction, so suiting objectives *A* to *F* listed earlier, and prospective contractors can be asked to compete on the basis of the total cost of a project. A potential disadvantage to the promoter is that to get this competition between contractors he has to decide the scope of a project and all that matters to him in quality of work, restraints on access to a site, etc. before inviting tenders. One way of reducing this problem is to invite prospective contractors to make proposals on design and all such questions before deciding what to specify in inviting tenders from them.

If a promoter cannot or will not decide all the performance required by that stage of a project, the proposed terms of contract can include provisions for the promoter to issue the remainder later or to order **variations** to the specified works, as is usual in traditional contracts in Britain, but with the risk of making the agreement more complex and creating a basis for claims from a contractor for extra time or money.

Excepted risks

A principle of all the above types of contract is that a contractor takes the risks of controlling his costs. Experienced promoters usually limit these to the risks which contractors can best control. The typical terms of contracts are therefore that contractors take the cost risks of planning to employ people and plant efficiently, purchasing materials, and the performance of subcontractors, though with some exceptions, and promoters take the cost risks of changes in legislation (for instance affecting taxation), escalation (at least during many lengthier contracts), design errors (unless a contractor is responsible), and variations.

Other risks are usually shared, for instance those of strikes, accidents, earthquakes, riots or war. If such a supervening event occurs, a contractor is usually entitled to an extension to the period for completing the works, but has to bear his costs of a longer use of plant; the promoter has to bear his own losses that may be due to later use of the project, but of course depending on the terms of the contract.

The words 'force majeure' are sometimes used to mean risks such as earthquakes, riots and war that are due to overwhelming forces not under the control of the parties to a contract, but these words are only a label for a concept and have no precise meaning or standard effect on a contract under English law. The words 'excepted risks' are used rather similarly in some contracts, but what is meant should be defined in a contract.

Management contracts

The description **management contractor** is used in the UK to mean a contractor employed to plan, define and perhaps direct the work of other contractors on behalf of a promoter. The management contractor thus provides part or all of a promoter's team for a project. Employment of a contractor in this way can be combined with use of any of the types of contracts for construction described in this chapter.

The potential advantages to a promoter in employing a management contractor are that his project team is provided with contracting and construction expertise, and that this service can be hired and fired. To achieve a single team, a promoter has to integrate the management contractor's staff with his own.

Direct labour or direct works

Instead of employing a contractor a promoter may have projects constructed by his own construction department, known in the UK as **direct labour** or **direct works**.

Usually such promoters also have their own design department. In examples in municipal authorities in Britain the two departments are managed separately. They are linked for the construction of a project by an internal order which is in effect the equivalent of a contract that specifies the scope, standards and price of the works as if the departments were separate companies. This arrangement has the advantages of making clear the responsibilities for project cost due to design and due to methods of construction, and of developing expertise in each type of work. Except that disputes between the departments would be managerial rather than legal problems, these internal 'contracts' can be similar to commercial agreements between organizations. Contractual principles and this book are therefore relevant to them.

In some cases a direct works department competes with independent contractors to construct the promoter's projects, and therefore tenders as if separate.

Contractor as promoter

Similarly if a contractor promotes as well as constructs a project he may need to separate these two roles because different expertise and responsibilities are involved in deciding whether to proceed with the project and then how to construct it. Separation of these responsibilities may also be required because others are participating in financing the project. For all such projects except small ones an internal contract may therefore be appropriate to define who is to be responsible for design, construction and risks.

Bibliography

Civil engineering procedure, 4th ed, Institution of Civil Engineers, London, 1986.

Thompson P.A., *Organization and economics of construction*, (2nd edition due 1989), McGraw-Hill Book Co, Maidenhead, 1981.

Hayes R.W. et al, *Management contracts*, report 100, Construction Industry Research & Information Association, London, 1983.

3 Terms of payment

'Quid pro quo'

Money is the primary measure used by promoters when they are selecting a project, assessing their risks, comparing prospective contractors' tenders, and reviewing the immediate and the longer-term results. Value for money is thus the concern of promoters, and in effect money for value the concern of contractors. In planning a contract a promoter should therefore consider what terms of payment are likely to motivate contractors to try to achieve the objectives of a project.

Payment by price or by cost?

The choice for a promoter is to pay for work by **price** or by cost, a price strictly meaning an amount stated in a contract that the contractor is to be paid and actual cost is his risk. In the alternative of payment by cost the promoter takes this risk. Payment by price is therefore preferred by most promoters.

The choice between payment by price and by cost is complicated in practice by one being used for much of the work for a project under a contract but the other for the remainder. Payment by price can also be modified by agreement in a contract that the works may be varied, or that escalation costs will be reimbursed, but in principle the two alternatives offer a choice between the contractor and the promoter making the decisions that govern whether the contractor's resources are used economically.

Lump sum payment

The description 'lump sum' is generally used to mean that a single payment is made when the works are completed. It is preferred by promoters who place performance contracts, that is when a contractor is responsible for design and construction to a price,

12

and the promoter does not expect to have to specify further detail or changes. Most lump sum payment contracts are therefore price based.

Lump sum contracts have the potential advantages to promoters that the contractors take the risks of actual costs being greater than the contract prices, and that being paid for performance should be an incentive to contractors to avoid delays to the works. They are appropriate for projects that are fully designed before prospective contractors are invited to tender and completion of the works on time or ahead of programme is more valuable to the promoters than second thoughts on design or changes to any terms of what has been agreed. To a promoter a potential disadvantage is that changes he decides to make could lead to claims from a contractor for extra time and payment for affecting his planned use of resources, though this could have the indirect advantage to a promoter that the risk of such claims could deter his staff or advisers from proposing changes.

Lump sum terms of payment can be quite simple, especially if only a single payment is due for completion of performance. In practice payment is usually in stages, for example most of the lump sum being paid for substantial completion of the works so that the promoter can start to use them, and the **retention** sum being paid a year later if the contractor has performed all his outstanding obligations. Potential disadvantages of these complications are that what is 'substantial' completion needs to be agreed. Like all requirements in a specification, it should ideally be defined quantitatively so that its achievement can be demonstrated by a simple test. The amount of retention money also needs to be sufficient to be an incentive to a contractor, as discussed later.

Lump sum payment is usual in contracts for the design and supply of mechanical, electrical and process plant.

Milestone and planned progress payment systems

Payment to a contractor can be based upon his achieving 'milestones', meaning defined stages of progress. This has the potential advantage to a promoter that a contractor has an incentive to proceed with his work, and to a contractor that he is paid sooner after incurring the costs. The disadvantages are that the milestones have to be defined and their achievement proved, as above, in agreeing to pay for substantial completion, and to avoid

13

doubts and disputes they may need to be defined in detail.

Use of the word milestones usually means that payment is based upon achieving stages of completion of the works, i.e. progress in constructing what a promoter wants. Payment based upon achieving defined stages of a contractor's activities is sometimes known as a 'planned payment' scheme.

These terms of payment are common in contracts for construction in developing countries, particularly when a contractor is responsible for design, construction and arranging for loans to finance the costs of a project.

Bills of quantities (BoQ)

Bills of quantities as used in UK construction contracts traditionally list each item of work to be done for the promoter under a contract, for instance a quantity of concrete for foundations to a quality defined in an accompanying specification and as shown on drawings.

The bills are usually prepared with the drawings for issue to prospective contractors to be the basis of their tenders. Or the contractors may be required to prepare ('take-off') a bill of quantities from the drawings. In either case a standard method of measurement of each item can be specified, typically one established for use in civil engineering. The contractors are required to include the BoQ with their tenders having inserted a **rate**, i.e. price per unit quantity, or a lump sum price for each item as instructed.

Payment to a contractor is usually based upon the quantities of the items completed each month and payments made at the rate for each item multiplied by the quantity completed up to the total quantity shown in the bills when tenders were invited, less a percentage of retention. In these contracts the total price is therefore a lump sum divided into many small lumps as a basis for paying for progress.

The potential advantage to a promoter of this basis of payment is that it should induce performance. It has the important effect that a contractor is paid soon after incurring costs and therefore does not have to finance most of his contract cash needs. This may have the advantage to a promoter that the total cost of construction is reduced if he can borrow to finance projects at less cost than can a contractor.

Requiring prospective contractors to give rates for each item in a bill of quantities makes it possible for the promoter to compare their prices in detail and so assess whether the contractors have understood the scope of the work and how they have allowed for risks. Also it may be that the requirement for contractors to analyze their costs for each item of work before entering into a contract has the advantage to all parties that their work is well planned and construction should proceed to time and safely.

Comparison of the rates tendered in a BoQ by competing contractors has to be carried out thoroughly to see if any prices offered by some contractors for items expected to be completed early in construction are relatively higher than the later ones, so that these contractors would obtain greater payment early during a contract without their total tender prices being different. This is one form of what is known as 'loading' the rates in a tender.

One disadvantage of BoQs is that their preparation and administration is more complex and expensive, relative to a simple lump sum basis of payment, for all parties. A BoQ should therefore be used when it is a cost-effective method of controlling payments to a contractor.

Remeasurement and variations

A promoter can plan to make more extensive use of bills of quantities by establishing in the invitation for tenders for a contract that the rates in the accepted tender will be the basis for payment for changes in the works if ordered under a contract. This use of BoQ rates can be agreed to operate in two ways:

● Additional or lesser quantities of any item that are ordered by the promoter will be paid for at the BoQ rates per unit quantity, within a reasonable or stated range of change.

● Rates for new or altered categories of work ordered will be based upon the rates for related items in the BoQ, as far as is reasonable.

The first of these two provisions is known as **remeasurement, admeasurement** or **measure-and-value**. The second is usually a term of traditional contracts to provide what may be needed for payment for variations. Both have evolved in civil engineering in the UK in contracts for new work. They are now also used in contracts for repairs and maintenance of structures, etc., and for

15

mechanical and electrical work such as pipe and cable installation, when types of work can be predicted but the quantities and the conditions of access are uncertain until the time of doing the work.

The potential advantage to a promoter of a remeasurement basis of payment is that a contract can be agreed using approximate quantities and therefore before design is complete or all site needs are known, and payment is made only for actual quantities of work done. The advantage to a promoter of provisions for variations is that design changes can be planned using the BoQ rates to estimate their costs and to choose the cheapest of alternative ways of making proposed changes.

A general criticism of these uses of BoQ is that they provide a facility for making changes which are avoidable and allow design and other decisions which could be final before inviting tenders to be made only provisionally or postponed. Obvious disadvantages are that the BoQ is more complex and expensive to prepare and measure, and that there can be disputes about the effects of changes on the tendered rates.

Other risks to a promoter in inviting tenders for a contract under which payment will be based upon a BoQ and remeasurement are that the method of measurement used in compiling the BoQ may result in rates not being representative of the relative costs of work to a contractor, and prospective contractors when tendering may insert relatively high rates for the items in a BoQ they expect may increase in quantity, and lower rates for those that may decrease. Some of the loading of rates may be detected by comparing every rate from every contractor with independent data on costs of work.

Time-related and method-related costs

A traditional BoQ provides a basis for paying a contractor in proportion to quantities of accepted work. Not all a contractor's costs are proportional to these quantities. For instance, a variation may cause a change to the type of plant required, as well as amounts of materials. A design change or a delay for which the promoter is liable to pay may cause plant or other resources to be idle. To establish a basis for paying for these in proportion to cost a BoQ can therefore include items for the prospective contractors to insert rates for their time-related costs and lump sums for their method-related costs.

Time-related costs are also known as liquidated prolongation costs, indicating that an agreed amount is paid per week, day, etc. of delay for which a promoter is liable.

Prime cost items

A prime cost item is one listed in a main contract BoQ to allow the promoter to obtain equipment from a third party for the main contractor to install.

The 'prime cost' is agreed between the promoter and the third party. The item in the BoQ indicates to prospective contractors that they must be prepared to undertake to install the item. In tendering they are invited to state their lump sum prices or percentage additions to the prime cost for the installation and other responsibilities specified for such an item.

If a prime cost item is not used a contractor may be entitled to payment of the profit he expected to earn from it, depending on the terms of the contract.

Provisional sums

If a part of the scope of the works is uncertain at the time of inviting tenders a BoQ can be issued to the prospective contractors showing a 'provisional sum' for it and the terms of contract then state that the scope and price for it will be decided during the contract. By this means the contractors are warned that they must be prepared to carry out the item of work once defined, but usually under these contracts the promoter has the option not to use a provisional sum.

Payment for preliminaries

Many civil engineering contracts in Britain include items for some payment to a contractor for completion of site facilities for construction and for the ordering of some materials. These terms are intended to induce a contractor to make a quick start to his work because of the incentive of being paid the costs soon after incurring them.

The potential advantage to both parties is that the contractor's risks and financing costs should be less. The promoter has to meet the financing cost instead, but may be able to do so more cheaply than can a contractor. The potential risk to the promoter is that the value of the early payment may be lost if the contractor subsequently fails to proceed with construction. Protection against this

17

can be arranged by requiring the contractor to provide a performance **bond** as a condition of the advance payment.

Schedules of rates

Schedules of rates are similar to bills of quantities in listing the work to be performed item by item and tenderers are required to price each per unit quantity. They are different in practice in the extent that the rates are expected to be related to the total quantities of work actually done compared to the amounts expected when inviting tenders.

In some contracts the rates from a contractor are intended to be the basis of payment for any quantity of an item. This concept offends reality, as costs depend not only upon quantities of materials but also upon how economically plant and labour are employed by continuous work. In other cases the contractors when tendering are asked to state rates per unit of items on the basis of indications of possible total quantities in a defined period. In these the basis of payment is therefore intended to be a more flexible version of a BoQ.

Schedules of rates are used in civil engineering for some preparatory and site exploration work, contracts for design, demolition, repairs and maintenance. They have the advantage of establishing a basis for payment when types of work but not quantities or continuity can be certain, but at the risk to promoters that tenderers will state rates that allow for very uneconomic use of resources.

Schedules of rates based upon approximate quantities are also used as the basis for payment in contracts for the installation of pipework and cables in mechanical, electrical and process plant construction.

For some public projects in the UK the promoter publishes a schedule with rates inserted for every item and tenderers for a contract are required to state their rates as ± percentages of these rates.

Variations basis for a lump sum contract

A bill of quantities or a schedule of rates may be used with an otherwise lump sum based contract for tenderers to state rates which will provide a means of paying for variations ordered under such contracts.

Retention money

As stated earlier, many civil engineering contracts include a term stating that a percentage of payments due to a contractor as a lump sum or based on a BoQ will be retained by the promoter until a specified period (one year is usually the maximum) after taking over the works. The amount is then 'released' (paid) if the contractor has completed his obligations such as rectifying poor work.

The potential advantage to a prómoter is that a contractor should have the incentive to complete his obligations. In practice this may not be effective if the contractor calculates that his resources can earn more if used instead on work for other contracts. To anticipate this a promoter can have specified a large percentage retention of payments when inviting tenders, but at the risk that the tender prices will therefore be higher to meet the greater costs and risks to the contractors.

A contractor does not cease to be liable to the promoter or to other parties for defects or their consequences by being paid the retention money, but a contract can include agreement that liability to the promoter is limited from that time.

Contract price adjustment for escalation (CPA)

In price-based contracts either the promoter or contractor can take most of the risks of predicting the effects of inflation or deflation on the costs of labour and materials to be used for a project.

A lump sum, BoQ or other price-based contract can therefore include a term that contractors' tender prices are to be based upon costs of the relevant labour and materials known at a stated date before tendering, and that the payments due under the contract will be adjusted to reimburse the changes in these costs. Data on these changes in costs are published for the construction and other industries in the UK, and methods for calculating the effects on contract prices established. By this means a contractor may be paid much of extra costs due to inflation, though the agreed methods of calculating them may not reimburse all the effects.

Contract terms based upon this concept are common in civil engineering in this country for construction expected to take at least one year. Some promoters only agree it if expected to take at least two years. Inclusion of such terms has the potential advantages that contractors do not have to price high enough to be safe if inflation is above predicted rates and promoters have

19

to pay for only the real costs so far as measured by the chosen method. A disadvantage for promoters is that they cannot be sure in advance what the extra costs will be. Directly and indirectly they also have to pay their own and the contractor's costs of calculating and handling the extra payments.

If a contract does not include such terms, the tender prices from contractors are likely to be higher in times of inflation, but the promoter knows that the total contract price he will be due to pay will be independent of inflation. He may also expect that contractors will have the incentive to complete construction more rapidly if inflation is likely to cause their costs to rise rapidly, but with the extreme risk that a contractor may lose so much money as to go out of business before completing the works.

Contracts without CPA terms are often referred to as **fixed price**, but this meaning of those words should not be relied upon.

Cost-reimbursable and dayworks payment

In contrast to all the above are cost-based terms of payment. The simplest form of these is a contract under which a promoter 'reimburses' (pays) all a contractor's costs of work on a project, plus usually a fixed sum or percentage for financing, overheads and profit. More complicated is a contract under which the costs-plus of achieving all satisfactory or acceptable work are reimbursed, but not the costs of rejected work.

Under such contracts the promoter either directs or supervises a contractor's use of resources, in effect employing the contractor as an extension of his own organization. They are used when the type of resources likely to be needed can be predicted but what is to be produced will remain uncertain until near the time for doing it. This type of contract is used for design studies, development, some repair, demolition and emergency work.

The advantage to a promoter is that work can be started as soon as defined and changes made or work repeated without any basis for disputes that a contractor will incur costs not covered by prices. The disadvantage to a promoter is that the contractor is not responsible for the economic use of his resources and cost control. The advantage to a contractor is that his risks are limited, but so is the prospective profit as this is the only price basis for competition between prospective contractors for such a contract and is usually then fixed.

One basis for reimbursable cost-based payment in British civil engineering contracts is what is known as a **dayworks** section of an otherwise price-based contract. Contractors when tendering are required to state rates per hour or per day for being paid for using their employees and plant as instructed by a promoter, so providing a means of proceeding with emergency or unexpected work in addition to the scope of work specified in a price-based contract.

Target-incentive contracts

A development of the reimbursable type of contract is that a promoter and a contractor agree at the start a probable cost for a then uncertain scope of work, but also agree that the contractor will share savings in cost relative to the target but be reimbursed less than costs-plus if the target is exceeded. The target can be agreed as a lump sum, or in detailed BoQ items.

This basis of payment is intended to induce a contractor to be economic in his use of resources though the scope of the works is uncertain when making the contract.

The potential advantage to a promoter is that both parties should have an incentive to limit the costs, and to a contractor that at least his costs will be reimbursed. Problems may arise if the basis of the target is not precise or is changed, as the parties may then dispute whether work found to be needed was to be expected to be included or is to alter the target.

Liquidated damages terms

Many engineering and construction contracts include terms under which a contractor is liable to pay liquidated damages to a promoter for a breach of contract such as being late in completing construction. The obligation to pay depends upon the terms agreed and whether a breach occurs. Usually a contractor is not liable for a breach due to the promoter, excepted risks or other causes beyond a contractor's control.

The intention of liquidated damages terms is to induce contractors to perfom their contractual obligations. The simplest example is agreement that a specific payment is due to a promoter for a specific amount of delay in completing work.

Prior agreement in a contract on payment for a breach is the alternative to proceeding with a legal action for damages through the courts. The advantage of this prior agreement should be that its results are more predictable and quicker.

The motivation it is intended to give the contractor to perform his obligations is a potential advantage, but as observed about retention money, a contractor may prefer to incur the risk of having to pay a known amount as liquidated damages rather than spend his money to avoid a breach. Under English law damages are viewed as compensation for loss, not as punishment. The amount payable as liquidated damages cannot be so great as to be a terrorizing penalty (see Appendix C).

A contract could include a term for payment of liquidated damages by the promoter to the contractor, for instance for the risk that the promoter may encounter delay in being allowed by others to give the contractor access to site or permission to start construction.

Bibliography

Horgan M.O'C., *Competitive tendering for engineering projects*, Spon, London, 1984.

Perry J.G. et al, *Target and cost-reimbursable construction contracts*, report 85, Construction Industry Research & Information Association, London, 1982.

Barnes N.M.L. et al, *Financial control*, Engineering management guide, Thomas Telford Ltd, London (in preparation).

4 Contract documents

'An oral contract isn't worth the paper it is
written on'
— *attributed to Sam Goldwyn*

Contracts do not have to be written or otherwise recorded to be
enforceable. It depends upon the law of a country, but in most
the purchasing of food and many other goods from shops provides
obvious examples of transactions that we expect to be satifactorily
based upon oral agreements. The terms of the agreement can be
implied by the behaviour of the parties and common practice. The
agreement is enforceable if there is evidence of an agreement that
meets the legal rules on what is a contract. (A summary of the
rules under English law is given in Appendix C).

Written records

Recording the terms of an agreement in **writing** is the usual way
of planning to be able to prove that there was an intention to be
committed contractually and to show what was agreed. In commercial contracts such as for construction it is up to the parties
to agree to record a contract on paper. It is generally wise to do
so in agreeing terms that are complex or if the performance of the
contract is not immediate or may be affected by uncertainties and
other risks. Written contracts are normal practice in civil engineering and the rest of the construction industry, not least because many
promoters have internal rules requiring this or those who finance
their projects require it. Genuine or imagined urgency can be a
reason for oral commitments, but such rules and the common
wisdom dictate that oral agreements should be confirmed in writing
as soon as practicable.

Negotiating 'subject to contract' is common in England, and
many promoters, contractors and other organizations issue instructions internally to their employees that communications externally
with other organizations must be conducted only by authorized

23

individuals and be sent or confirmed in writing. Despite this they may be committed contractually by the statements or actions of an employee, even if unintentionally. Behaving as if there was a contract may be evidence, depending upon the circumstances, the relevant law and the proof it accepts.

Many organizations prefer to include in their contracts a clause saying that only written communications will be recognized contractually, but this is not effective before the contract is agreed. The greatest risks of entering into unwise or uncertain oral commitments are during negotiations for a contract, especially when there is haste to agree a price, other commercial terms or detail of the scope of work or specifications. Parallel negotiation of these between different people needs particular care to plan and coordinate what can be offered and what is acceptable. Everyone involved therefore needs to be aware of how agreements become contractual. When promoters employ consultants, consulting engineers or others to assist or take the lead in negotiations, these and their employees should be informed of their authority to commit a promoter and whether they can do so orally.

How much to record?

If it is wise to agree or confirm agreements in writing, there are problems in deciding how much detail should be recorded. To include everything however obvious is safe, but may not be worth the cost and can create contract documents so lengthy that users cannot comprehend them and are tempted to ignore or assume what is in them. The guiding principle should be to record agreement on only whatever may be doubtful or is different from standard *and* relates to needs or potential problems which could seriously affect the objectives of a project.

Separate documents

For a small amount of construction it is usually sufficient for a contract to consist of a drawing and an exchange of letters. A drawing can show the location and amount of work. The materials can be specified on it, or these and the construction period, price and other terms that matter to the parties stated in a letter. If the agreement is the result of a series of letters and replies, what is known as offer and counter-offers, one final letter should state all that has been agreed and replace all previous communications so as to leave no doubt as to what has been offered and accepted.

To avoid these doubts on all but small projects the practice has evolved of stating the various terms of a contract in a set of documents. These can be lengthy, but some can be the same for many contracts and so do not have to be prepared anew each time. The set of documents tradtionally used in UK civil engineering contracts is:

o Agreement
o Conditions of contract
o Drawings
o Specification
o Bill of quantities.

Practice varies as to which of the above documents contains some of the terms of a contract. Where a term is included in the set of documents is not significant for it to be part of a contract, but it is preferable for all the industry to be consistent to reduce the risks of omitting or duplicating items, and to help readers to remember where to look for items. A simple check list for planning the function of each document is provided by the words *what, where, who, when, how, what if*, as shown overleaf.

An important rule is that nothing should be stated twice or any term summarized elsewhere, in order to avoid being inconsistent. For this reason, the duties of the parties required by law, such as under health and safety legislation, should not be restated or summarized in a contract. Under English law these **implied terms** are automatically part of a contract.

Planning and co-ordination

The set of documents does need to be planned for each contract, to make sure that it records what matters.

The documents listed in the table are those used in the traditional procedure in the UK based upon competitive tendering. The same functions are needed in any contract whether based upon competition or not, but in every case the documents should be planned to suit the objectives, size and nature of the construction work required and the demands on a contractor and others.

As documents different in function are usually prepared by different groups of people, the set for a contract should be co-ordinated by one person.

	Function	Usual contract document
What?	Type of project	Specification — should give the name and short description of the project
	Scope, shape, size	Drawings
	Quality of work	Specification
How much?	Amount of work	Bill of quantities
	Amounts of bond, retention, insurance, liquidated damages	Appendix to tender
Where?	Location	Drawings
When?	Period for completion	Appendix to tender
	Payment	Conditions of contract
Who?	Parties	Agreement
	Name of the engineer	Invitation for tenders
	Responsibilities	Conditions of contract
How?	Procedures	Conditions of contract
What if?	Prior agreement on liabilities and procedures	Conditions of contract

Particular and general documents

What is to be constructed, by who, where, when and at what price has to be agreed for every project. The drawings, specification and bill of quantities are therefore particular to a contract. The form of these may be similar from project to project, and some standard detail used, especially in compiling a specification, but as a whole they have to be prepared anew.

The concept of separate **conditions of contract** is that these should contain the terms which should not vary from project to project. They therefore contain terms which state the nature of the responsibilities of the parties, relationships with sub-contractors, and procedures for resolving 'how' and 'what if' questions. These are the terms which establish who is liable for what and provide the basis for action on problems. They can be vital for avoiding as well as solving doubts and differences. They therefore need to be understood and used by all concerned with achieving successful contractual relationships.

Bibliography

Guidance on the preparation, submission and consideration of tenders for civil engineering contracts in the UK, Institution of Civil Engineers, London, 1983.
Notes on documents for civil engineering contracts, FIDIC, Lausanne, 1977.

5 Model conditions of contract

'Rules and models destroy genius and art'
— *Hazlitt*

Sets of model conditions of contract have been evolved in the UK
and other countries for use in construction, and also models for
use in mechanical, electrical and process engineering work. These
models have been drafted by professional engineering institutions,
trade associations and legal advisers, in consultation with others
interested, and revised and redrafted from time to time to overcome problems and to incorporate changes in the law.

General conditions of contract

The models published by the Institution of Civil Engineers and
others are sometimes referred to as 'general' conditions of contract, indicating that they consist of clauses expected to be relevant to a range of type of project and are intended to be used in
conjunction with drawings, a specification and other documents
that define the particular scope of the works.

The various models listed below differ in the extent that a contractor is responsible for design and how risks are divided between
a promoter and a contractor. The detailed wording is also very
different in these models, but all include clauses on the nature of
the responsibilities of the parties and establish procedures for the
approval of programmes, safety, sub-letting, insurance, patents,
delays, variations, inspection, taking over and acceptance.

These model conditions are recommended by their sponsors for
use complete as drafted. Printed copies can be purchased from
their publishers. Copies need not be included in a set of contract
documents provided that an accurate reference is given to the title
and edition to be taken as part of the terms of a contract. Some
promoters prefer to continue to use previous editions of model conditions rather than the latest. In these cases making clear which

edition is meant is obviously important.

Note that 'terms of sale' is the more common description for various sets of conditions of contract for the sale of manufactured equipment, materials, etc.

The models

The following model forms are commonly used or adapted for use in construction and engineering contracts in the UK:

- *Conditions of contract for civil engineering works*, published by the Institution of Civil Engineers, the Association of Consulting Engineers and the Federation of Civil Engineering Contractors. (5th edition published in 1973. Some amendments issued since). Known briefly as '*the ICE conditions*', '*the ICE contract*' or '*ICE 5*'.

- *Conditions of contract for minor works*, Institution of Civil Engineers, 1987. (In green covers, but note that other sets of conditions are called the 'Green Book'.)

- *GC/Works/1* Conditions of Contract for Construction, prepared by the Property Services Agency, published by H.M. Stationery Office.

- *Standard form of building contract*, published for the JCT by RIBA Publications Ltd. (Different forms are produced for private and local authority use, and with or without quantities, a design-and-build, and management contracts, at various dates).

- *Conditions of contract for complete process plants*, published by the Institution of Chemical Engineers, in two forms:

o For lump sum contracts, the '*Red Book*' (revised edition published in 1981).

o For reimbursable contracts, the '*Green Book*' (1976). (Revision now being considered).

- *Conditions of contract for the purchase of mechanical or electrical equipment*, published by the Institution of Mechanical Engineers, the Institution of Electrical Engineers and the Association of Consulting Engineers. (Alternative forms for the supply of plant with or without erection, and for home or for overseas use published and revised at various dates).

- *Conditions of sale for machinery and equipment*, published by the British Electrotechnical and Allied Manufacturers Association (1979).

Also published by various trade organizations and others are sets of general conditions for specific classes of work such as heating and ventilating systems for large buildings or for fabrication work for process plants.

Standards or models?

All the above are **models** rather than UK standards, as there are several different sets of such conditions in use, and also many of the larger promoters use their own variants of the ICE, GC/Works and other conditions.

New models

The BPF produced a new contract system for building projects, in 1983.

The ICE is preparing a set of conditions for design-and-construct contracts and has commissioned a draft for a new style of main contract intended to be for a wide range of types of work and terms of payment, to be clearer and simpler, and to be designed to provide a better basis for project management.

International models

- *Conditions of contract (International) for works of civil engineering construction*, published by FIDIC, 4th edition, 1987 (also known as the 'Red Book'). Part I consists of general conditions recommended for any civil engineering project. Part II consists of guidance on the drafting of conditions of particular application to a project.

- *General conditions for works overseas*, European Development Fund.

- *Conditions of contract (International) for electrical and mechanical works*, published by FIDIC, 3rd edition, 1988 (known as the 'Yellow Book').

A European model for construction work for public authorities throughout the EC is likely to be produced by the European Commision before 1992.

Duties and powers

In the UK model conditions the duties (obligations) of a party are indicated by the wording '... shall ...'. Powers (or options) are indicated by the wording '... may ...'.

Number of contracts

All the sets of model conditions listed except those for mechanical and electrical machinery and equipment are drafted for one contractor to be the main one employed on a site.

Use of the models

The potential advantages of using model conditions are that they have been drafted mainly by people experienced in engineering and construction, they are intended to provide a basis for settling problems reasonably and fairly, the wording has been considered carefully to try to make sure that it is clear and unambiguous, and they are published and available for immediate use so that copies do not need to be included in a set of contract documents. Use of one model for many projects should have the potential advantage that the clauses become known and understood.

Unfortunately, most have become longer as a result of successive revisions, and can be too complex to be cost-effective for all but the largest projects. Some are also not easily understood. They can be simplified by omitting clauses or parts of clauses, for instance to use the ICE contract without bills of quantities, but this has to be done with care to make sure that the resulting terms are consistent.

One set of model conditions for all civil engineering contracts is an ideal for reducing variety, uncertainty and some costs to all parties. The many promoters who use variants of the above models or add extra clauses may consider that their needs and conditions are special. In fact the differences may not be worth their cost; probably far more important to successful results is attention by the promoter of a project to making the best possible decisions on the objectives, scope and the design requirements of a project, and then controlling changes to these once a contract has been agreed for construction.

Choice of conditions

All the model conditions listed are drafted in the expectation

31

that the promoter will decide the choice of conditions of contract and specify the choice when inviting tenders.

If no conditions are specified in an invitation for tenders, contractors can be expected to fill this vacuum by proposing a set. Alternatively, when tendering in response to an invitation which specifies a set of conditions a contractor may propose modified or different conditions. In either case the promoter might respond by rejecting part or all of the contractor's proposals, but the exchange of proposals might continue in a process of offer and counter offer, etc. Care is needed before entering into the contract to make sure that both parties agree what conditions apply.

Bibliography

Marks R.J. et al, *Aspects of civil engineering procedure*, 3rd ed, Pergamon Press, Oxford, 1985.

Sawyer J.G. and Gillott C.A., *The FIDIC conditions: Digest of contractual relationships and responsibilities*, 2nd ed, Thomas Telford Ltd, London, 1985. (Text and commentary on the 3rd edition (now superseded) of the FIDIC conditions (international) for civil engineering construction — new edition in preparation).

JCT guides to forms of building contracts, RIBA Publications Ltd, London.

Conditions of engagement, Association of Consulting Engineers, London.

Manual of the BPF system, British Property Federation, London, 1983.

6   The engineer

'Upon this Rock will I build'
— *Matthew ch XVIII*

In the ICE and other British model conditions a person named under a contract as 'the Engineer' has powers and duties to instruct and supervise a contractor. Equivalents in some British or Commonwealth country contracts are 'the Superintending Officer' and 'the Supervising Officer', and in building contracts 'the Architect', but with their powers and duties varying considerably from contract to contract.

Note that the initial capital letter in the word **Engineer** is used to indicate the particular person named in a contract.

Independence

This concept of a third party role as defined in construction contracts was established when consulting engineers became recognised as professional advisers independent of contractors. Traditionally design was a consulting engineer's first responsibility. Formalization of functions of the Engineer to administer a contract for construction followed. The role continues today, though the powers and duties vary greatly, and many promoters name a member of their staff as the Engineer.

Authority and communications

In supervising a contractor under the ICE conditions (and other models) the Engineer is an agent of the promoter. It is the Engineer who accepts or rejects work by a contractor — under the terms of these traditional contracts a promoter has no rights to do so. The Engineer alone and independently has the power to allow a contractor more time, depending upon reasons stated in a contract, may order a contractor to vary the works, and has a duty to decide the payments due to a contractor.

The Engineer is not a party to the contract for the construction of the works. He is the channel of communications with a contractor on all matters relevant to the satisfactory completion of the works under the contract. The Engineer must have his separate contract of employment or service, as indicated in Fig. 2.

Servant of the contract

The Engineer in this role illustrated in Fig. 2 has been described as a 'servant of the contract', meaning that his powers and duties are those stated in the contract terms and he is obliged to do what they say he shall, otherwise the contract is being breached. The concept is that the Engineer is a named individual who has the expertise, knowledge of a contract and time to use it, but he may delegate his powers to others unless a contract says he may not.

The potential advantage of this system to a promoter is that as the Engineer is the single channel of communications with a con-

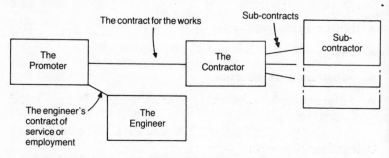

THE TRADITIONAL CONTRACTUAL RELATIONSHIPS BETWEEN PROMOTER, ENGINEER AND CONTRACTOR

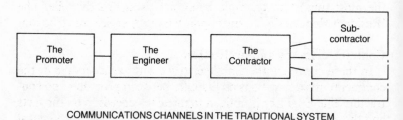

COMMUNICATIONS CHANNELS IN THE TRADITIONAL SYSTEM

Fig. 2. Authority and communications in the traditional contract system for civil engineering projects in Britain

tractor, he should be dedicated to a project, and should provide expert supervision and instructions on problems of construction. The obligation of the Engineer to decide the payments due should have the advantage to promoter and contractor that the results are reasonable and based upon fact, so that a promoter pays for the work actually required rather than the higher prices that contractors might have tendered if asked to bear all the construction risks.

A potential disadvantage to the promoter and contractor is that neither can be certain of the final scope and cost of the works until after construction is complete. This is a risk under any contract without the Engineer having such power; the difference is in whether claims such as for extra costs are settled by negotiation between the parties or by the Engineer under a duty to do so reasonably.

In a recent report to the ICE on the need for a new style of contract the role of the Engineer has been analysed as consisting of four possible functions:

● Project management

● Design

● Supervising construction

● Adjudicating on contractual disputes between Promoter and Contractor.

Delegation of powers

The ICE conditions permit the Engineer to delegate many of his powers to a person he names as the Engineer's representative, the most important example being a person usually called the 'Resident Engineer' on a site appointed to supervise construction.

Contract disputes and arbitration

In these contracts the Engineer has a duty as a servant of the contract to make decisions on disputes between promoter and contractor. The Engineer is obliged to make his decisions on the facts and the terms of a contract. He does not have the role or the legal status of an arbitrator, but most contracts also include an agreement that the Engineer's decision on a dispute may be further taken to an arbitrator.

35

International practice

The ICE and the FIDIC model conditions of contract are similar, particularly in being based upon the concept that the Engineer has powers as more than a representative of a promoter. This concept is not widely accepted outside Britain and some Commonwealth countries.

Bibliography

Functions of the engineer under the ICE conditions of contract, Guidance note No. 2A, Conditions of Contract Standing Joint Committee, 1977. (Defines the role of the Engineer as having duties independent of Promoter and Contractor).

A new style contract for engineering projects, Martin Barnes Project Management/Deloitte Haskins & Sells, report ref LAC/87/1R, Institution of Civil Engineers, 1987. (States the arguments for a new style of contract and analyses the possible functions of the Engineer).

Part II Contract administration

'Grounded on justice and right, well managed'
— *Milton*

Part I reviewed the choices to be considered in planning a contract, ending with notes on contract documents and the concept of the role of the Engineer.

Part II is an introduction to the ICE conditions, consisting of short chapters on the set of contract documents, contract start-up, sub-contracts, supervision, progress, payment, variations and handover. References are made to some important **clauses** in the ICE conditions by number, as indicated 'ICE cl ...'. Some references are also made to clauses in the FIDIC conditions.

It is the complete wording of a contract which governs its interpretation. These chapters should therefore be read together with the ICE conditions. Readers should not rely upon the indications of their scope given in these chapters.

In the ICE and FIDIC conditions a promoter of a project is called 'the Employer' when in contract with a contractor, but as noted earlier in this Guide the title 'Promoter' is used here throughout as in the ICE's booklet *Civil engineering procedure*.

Capital letters are used in the words Engineer and Contractor to indicate the particular ones named in a contract.

7 From tender to contract

A contract is made when a tender is accepted. In this chapter how the ICE conditions and related contract documents are designed to be used in the process of inviting tenders and agreeing a contract for civil engineering construction work is reviewed.

Invitation for tenders

In the traditional procedure using the ICE conditions the prospective contractors are invited to tender for a contract on the basis of detailed drawings, a specification and a bill of quantities issued to them by the Promoter or on his behalf.

The total price of such contracts is expected to be large in proportion to the costs of the provisional sums, prime cost items and dayworks ordered. Contracts using the ICE conditions are thus predominantly price-based. In them the risks to be taken by the Contractor should therefore be defined as precisely as possible and all relevant information given to tenderers.

A set of instructions to tenderers (ITT) is usually issued with these and has the following functions:

- Lists the documents

- States that the ICE conditions are to be part of the contract and gives the name of the person designated to be the Engineer.

- States whether bonds are required, the period that tenders must be open for acceptance, what information tenderers must provide (for instance whether a construction programme is required with tenders), and whether alternative designs, construction periods or other terms will be considered.

- Lists preferred and nominated sub-contractors (if any).

39

- States whether the optional clause on contract price fluctuations is to be part of the contract, and on a copy shows the price factors to be used.

- Specifies where and how tenders are to be submitted.

These instructions may also be used to draw the tenderers attention to important or unusual terms of the proposed contract, for instance safety requirements or restrictions on access to parts of a site, but these terms should not be repeated, paraphrased or summarized in the instructions.

The drawings, specification, conditions of contract and BoQ are sometime called 'tender documents'. They are the proposed contract documents.

Form of tender

A single page 'form of tender' and an appendix on the back of it are published with the ICE conditions.

This form provides a model letter to a promoter from a tenderer offering to enter into a contract for the works in conformity with the tender documents. The appendix provides a document for listing contract data, particularly the time for completion of the whole works (and for different sections, if required), amount of performance bond (if any), amount of insurance, rates of payment for liquidated damages, and period of **maintenance**. The times and amounts which the Promoter wishes to be fixed should be inserted in the appendix before inviting tenders. Copies with these amounts entered in should therefore be issued with invitations for tenders, and the remaining amounts should be entered by each contractor as part of his offer when tendering.

Using the wording of this model form of tender ensures that the tenderers confirm that they have based their offers on the tender documents. The appendix provides a basis for checking and comparing the amounts inserted by contractors.

All members of a joint venture or consortium of contractors should be required to sign a tender and to state that they are committed to their offer jointly and individually.

Form of agreement

A model 'form of agreement' is also published with the ICE conditions. This includes clauses stating that the Contractor will construct the works and the Promoter will pay, and lists the documents that are to be part of the agreement. The form is a single page needing only the date, names of the parties, a short description of the works and the title of the project or a contract reference number to be inserted.

The listing of the documents should state whether the selected tenderer's offer, letters, minutes of meetings or other documents exchanged prior to the agreement are to be part of the contract.

The form as printed is designed for signature under seal, but it can be used without this or the words in it adapted to be a letter from a promoter to a tenderer accepting his offer.

Drawings

The drawings which show what is to be constructed need to be listed in the tender documents, for instance at the start of the specification, or in an attachment to it. The tender drawings become the contract drawings unless others or modified drawings are agreed in negotiations between tendering and making a contract.

Once a contract is made the Engineer has the power and the duty under ICE cl 7 to supply modified or further drawings.

To achieve the potential advantages to a promoter of price-based contracts, the tender drawings for these should be complete and final. This applies to lump-sum and BoQ contracts. The inclusion of remeasurement and variation terms amounts to compromise between this ideal and recognition that uncertainties may lead to changes in the drawings after making a contract.

The ICE conditions are designed to be used in the traditional procedure in which what is to be constructed is specified to the Contractor. These conditions are not suitable for contracts in which the Contractor or his sub-contractors are responsible for the design of much of the permanent works.

Identity of documents

Published documents such as the ICE conditions and British Standards should be referred to by full title and edition. All the contract documents, including every drawing, should bear the project name and contract number (if any) stated at the start of the specification.

41

Conditions of contract

As noted earlier, the ICE conditions are intended to be used as printed, in which case only their title and edition need be specified to establish that they are part of a contract. Published with them are optional clauses on CPA, so that an agreement needs to state if these clauses are to be part of a contract.

ICE cl 1 is the only place in the model conditions as published for inserting the name of the Engineer. Rather than include a copy of the ICE conditions in the tender documents just for this purpose, the invitation for tenders usually states the name of the individual designated to be the Engineer.

Specification

The contract specification is the document for defining the required quality and standards of work and materials to be used, instead of stating these on the drawings. To be consistent, if a specification is needed for this reason, *all* qualitative requirements should be stated in it, not just those too detailed to show on the drawings.

The specification should begin by stating the project name and short description of the works. A contract number should also be stated if there is more than one contract for the whole project.

Ideally every requirement in a specification should include a definition of a test for proving whether or not it has been achieved. Requirements which cannot be proved as achieved or not should not be included. Phrases such as ' . . . to be of best quality . . . ' or 'sound workmanship' indicate an intention, but alone they postpone the problem of deciding what is good enough. These general phrases are useful only if specific requirements are also stated, so that if a contractor is failing to perform specific ones, the general ones can then be the basis of demanding more than the rectification of the errors and may be a basis for taking drastic action such as expelling the offending contractor.

The specification should state any special safety, health or welfare requirements on a site (or refer to a separate document such as an industrial promoter's own manual of site rules which states these).

If the contract will require the Contractor to work to a quality assurance plan, such as under BS5750, the specification should say so, and it should state the extent that approvals and documents on materials and methods will be required from the Contractor and from sub-contractors.

Some or all of a specification used for a previous project may appear to be appropriate for another. If appropriate, it is obviously easy to use it without alteration. Unfortunately there is a tendency for additions to be made because of the needs of a project, but for little to be removed. The result is that the documents get longer with time. The cost effects of increases in standards caused by adding to a specification can be great, but at the time of making them these additional costs may be less obvious than are the cost effects caused by increases in quantities of work that result from changes to drawings. Every addition to a specification also increases the risks of inappropriate or inconsistent requirements being included and mis-used or additions being made without checking the possible effects on related sections.

The specification for a contract should therefore be kept relatively simple. The following four principles can help:

- Specify only what is required by the scope of work shown on the drawings, rather than add to a specification used before.

- Include only those requirements which are worth their cost.

- Omit any requirement that cannot be proved as achieved.

- Refer to British Standards, safety regulations or other existing documents, not repeat their contents.

No dimensions or quantities of work should appear in a contract specification (except in the rare case of a contract for work which can be entirely defined in a specification and therefore needs no drawings or bill of quantities).

The specification should set out what form (if any) is to be used by the Contractor for monthly statements under ICE cl 60 to be the basis of payments.

Bill of quantities

A BoQ is usually prepared by or on behalf of a promoter with the drawings for issue with the invitations for tenders, but instead tenderers can be asked to prepare and price a BoQ. The greatest risks of errors and inconsistent detail in preparing contract documents are in listing the items of work in detail and calculating the quantities for a BoQ. The usual procedure of preparing it to issue to tenderers has the advantage that this work can be completed and checked in less of a hurry than usual in the limited period given for tendering.

Issue of a BoQ with invitations to tender also has the advantage to promoters that all the competing contractors' rates and prices can be compared on the same format. To achieve the advantages promoters pay the direct cost of the preparation of the BoQ instead of it being hidden in all contractors' prices.

The ICE conditions are written on the basis that the Contractor's tendered rates in a BoQ will be the basis of payment. If the tender documents include a BoQ, it should therefore be the only document which states quantities of work, rates and prices.

Under ICE cl 11(2) the Contractor's rates are deemed to cover all his obligations under a contract.

ICE cl 57 states that a BoQ shall be deemed to be in accordance with the ICE standard method of measurement (currently CESMM2) except where a BoQ shows the contrary. The appendix to the form of tender includes provision for an entry stating any amendment or modification adopted if different from standard. This should be entered in the appendix by whoever prepares a BoQ.

The BoQ for larger projects is best divided into sections, most typically corresponding to the physical areas or stages of work on site, plus usually a general section for items such as dayworks which may be used anywhere.

Performance bond

A model form of performance bond is also provided with the ICE conditions. The requirement that the Contractor shall provide a performance bond and the amount of bond should be shown in the appendix to the form of tender issued to prospective contractors when inviting their tenders.

ICE cl 10 states the obligations of the Contractor if a bond is required.

Other documents

ICE cl 1(e) defines a contract as consisting of the conditions of contract, specification, drawings, priced bill of quantities, the tender, the written acceptance and the contract agreement (if completed). No other documents exchanged prior to an agreement are therefore part of a contract under these conditions unless a term listing them is included.

Letters of intent

What are called 'letters of intent' sent to tenderers by promoters vary in their purpose and in their contractual effects. As the words indicate, a letter of intent is strictly a means of informing a tenderer of the intention to enter into a contract with him. It is used when a promoter's project team have decided which contractor they wish to be employed but have to or wish to delay making a contract, for instance because they have to obtain authority or action from their senior management or others for the contract to be made, or because they wish to negotiate changes with the intended contractor before being committed.

If the purpose is merely to inform a tenderer that his offer has been recommended for acceptance but that no obligation is intended on either side, the letter should say so. Such a letter does not commit either party to a contract.

If what is called a letter of intent asks a tenderer to extend the period his tender can be accepted beyond a time limit for this stated in it, the tenderer is free to decide whether to agree. He may offer to do so in return for an immediate payment or a change in the terms of the proposed contract.

A letter that asks a tenderer to start any of the work of a proposed contract would create a contract if accepted by the tenderer. The tenderer would not be bound to accept, but if he does the Promoter would then be committed, particularly to pay for the work done. A letter of intent which asks a tenderer to start any work should therefore contain the following:

- A statement that the Promoter intends to accept his tender.

- Instructions to proceed with work, specifying what work.

- A limit to cost to be incurred for the above.

- A statement that if the tender is subsequently not accepted the tenderer's costs for the work done will be paid, and a proposed basis for deciding the amount.

- A statement that the letter of intent becomes void on acceptance of the tender.

- A request to the tenderer to acknowledge receipt of the letter of intent and acceptance of its terms.

A letter of intent that attempts to commit a contractor without committing a promoter may not be legally enforceable, but a contractor can choose to respond to it by starting work and take the risk of not being paid.

Precedence between documents

Detail in a contract under English law takes precedence over general statements, but ICE cl 55(2) indicates that the drawings and specification take precedence over the BoQ if there is an error or omission between them. The Engineer has the duty to correct such errors or omissions.

ICE cl 5 states that the documents forming the contract are to be taken as mutually explanatory of one another. Under that clause the Engineer has the duty to take action on ambiguities or discrepancies in the documents.

FIDIC cl 5.2 establishes the following priority between documents:

- (1) Agreement (if completed).

- (2) Letter of acceptance.

- (3) Tender.

- (4) Part II conditions of contract (particular conditions agreed for that contract).

- (5) Part I conditions of contract (the FIDIC general conditions).

- (6) Any other document forming part of the contract.

Bibliography

Guide to the fifth: Explanatory notes for guidance to the ICE conditions of contract, fifth edition, 3rd ed, Institution of Civil Engineering Surveyors, 1986.

Abrahamson M.W., *Engineering law and the ICE contracts*, 3rd ed, Elsevier Applied Science Publications, Barking, 1975.

Duncan Wallace I.N., *Hudson's building and engineering contracts*, 10th ed, Sweet & Maxwell, London, 1970. Plus supplement, 1979.

Haslam J.E., *Writing engineering specifications*, Spon, London, 1988.
Civil engineering standard method of measurement, 2nd ed, Institution of Civil Engineers, London, 1985.
Barnes N.M.L., *The CESMM2 handbook*, Thomas Telford Ltd, London, 1986.

8 Contract start up

This chapter is in the form of a check list of actions once a contract under the ICE conditions comes into effect. All are actions for the Engineer. Some are needed immediately. The person designated to be the Engineer should therefore be prepared, by knowing the terms of a contract and assessing its possible risks. The list is a reminder of what may be needed.

- **Programme**   *Refer to*:

  o   Check that land for the works and rights of access
      have been acquired.★
  o   Check that the Promoter has obtained planning,
      financial and other approvals to proceed.★
  o   Notify the Contractor of date for commencement.   *ICE cl 41*
  o   Get the Contractor to submit a programme and   *ICE cl 14*
      description of arrangements and methods of   *and 13*
      construction. Inform the Contractor of consent or
      of requirements for changes and resubmission.
  o   Agree with the Contractor a programme for issue   *ICE cl 7*
      of further drawings.
  o   Agree with the Promoter a programme for
      decisions required from the Promoter.

- **Organization**

  o   Select, train and arrange induction of the
      Engineers' representatives and staff.
  o   Delegate to representatives, by letter to them   *ICE cl 2*
      copied to the Contractor.
  o   Approve the Contractor's agent.   *ICE cl 15*

- **Communications**
  - Agree with the Promoter a system and the scope of reports for Promoter and others.
  - Agree with the Promoter responsibilities for relationships with the press.
  - Arrange start-up meeting with the Contractor's agent and senior management, on site relationships, contract administration, safety, security and welfare. Invite the chief officers of local authorities, health and safety inspectorate, and others as appropriate.
  - Agree a system and scope of meetings, reports and instructions with the Contractor. *ICE cl 13 and 68*

- **Bonds and insurance**
  - Call for bonds from the Contractor, if contract requires them (for the Promoter). *ICE cl 10*
  - Call for insurance certificates from the Contractor (for the Promoter). *ICE cl 23*

- **Sub-contracts**
  - Call for list from the Contractor of proposed sub-contractors. *ICE cl 4*
  - Nominate or state dates when sub-contractors will be nominated for provisional sums and prime cost items. *ICE cl 58*

★ These actions should have been completed by the Promoter prior to entering into a contract for construction work.

Bibliography

Ballantyne J.K., *The Resident Engineer*, 2nd ed, Works Construction Guide, Thomas Telford Ltd, London, 1986.

Madge P., *Civil engineering insurance and bonding*, Thomas Telford Ltd, London, 1987.

9 Sub-contracts

It is usual for main contractors to emply sub-contractors to undertake sections of the works, for the same reasons as promoters employ main contractors. In this chapter the clauses in the ICE conditions on sub-contracting are discussed, particularly those which enable the Engineer to control or to decide the choice of sub-contractors.

Consent of the Engineer

ICE cl 4 states that the Contractor shall not sub-let any part of the works without the consent of the Engineer. In chapter 8 it was suggested that a list of proposed sub-contractors is required from the Contractor at the start of a contract in order for the Engineer to have time to consider each and the Contractor to propose an alternative if instructed by the Engineer.

Consent to the employment of a sub-contractor under ICE cl 4 does not relieve the Contractor from any liability or obligation under his contract.

Preferred sub-contractors

Time can be saved by including in the tender documents a list of the names of preferred potential sub-contractors for specified items of work, but with this is needed a term in the proposed main contract that makes clear whether the Contractor will be free to choose one of the preferred sub-contractors without needing the Engineer's consent to the terms of their sub-contract.

Nominated sub-contractors

In the ICE conditions there are two ways in which the Contractor can be obliged to employ a sub-contractor chosen by the

Promoter or the Engineer:

- Nomination in the tender documents for a prime cost item.

- An order by the Engineer to the Contractor under ICE cl 58 nominating a sub-contractor for a prime cost item or a provisional sum.

Any specialists, merchants, tradesmen or others nominated or ordered as above for the execution of any work or the supply of any goods, materials or services are defined as 'nominated sub-contractors'.

Nomination of a sub-contractor in the tender documents enables the Promoter to ask that sub-contractor to commence ordering materials or other work that needs to start before the main contract is agreed or to provide design information of components he is to supply for incorporation in the drawings for the main contract. It saves all the tenderers for a main contract the work and costs of obtaining quotations for the prime cost item from alternative sub-contractors.

Nomination under ICE cl 58 enables the Engineer to decide the scope and supplier of work that was left unspecified at the time of agreeing a main contract.

Under ICE cl 59(A) the Contractor can object to a nominated sub-contractor. The clause imposes a duty on the Engineer to resolve the problem. It gives the Engineer the power to reduce the liabilities of the Contractor if the latter has a reasonable objection to a nominated sub-contractor, or the Engineer can nominate an alternative sub-contractor, or make other arrangements for the work to be done.

Legal implications

ICE cl 59(A) is lengthy and complicated, as the action of instructing a contractor whom he is to employ is inconsistent with the principle that contractors take the risks of deciding the resources to use to construct the works. Brief comments on avoiding legal problems when nominating a sub-contractor are therefore given at the end of Appendix C.

Sub-contract terms

The Engineer could use his powers under ICE cl 4 to refuse to consent to a sub-contract if its terms are not as far as possible compatible with the main contract. Their compatibility may be important for achieving delivery, specification, liabilities for defects, insurance or safety. As in negotiating a main contract, care is needed when a potential sub-contractor tenders on his own quotation form that conditions of contract (or 'terms of sale') printed on the back are accepted only if suitable or if no better terms can be obtained.

The FCEC have published a 'blue' model set of conditions for sub-contracts to be compatible with the ICE conditions. This model is designed for sub-contracts for civil engineering work. It can be used for sub-contracts for the supply of mechanical and electrical components for a main contractor to install, but is not fully compatible with a main contract under the ICE conditions if a sub-contractor is also to be responsible for the design and performance of a system. In such a sub-contract, terms are needed on these responsibilities to the Promoter through the Contractor.

Bibliography
Form of sub contract for use in conjunction with the ICE conditions of contract, Federation of Civil Engineering Contractors, London, revised 1984.

10 Supervision

The purpose of supervision should be to try to be sure that work will be done correctly, safely and in time. It is achieved by establishing good relationships, knowing the obligations of the parties, anticipating possible problems, giving advice, and being prepared to use powers to give instructions.

Obligations

The model form of tender, form of agreement and cl 8 in the ICE conditions differ a little in how they define the Contractor's obligation to carry out the works. Fortunately the differences should not result in doubt that the Contractor undertakes to construct, complete, hand over and maintain the permanent works and to provide the materials, labour, plant, temporary works and management needed — except those stated in the contract to be provided by the Promoter or the Engineer. In the ordinary language of the industry the Contractor is thus responsible for construction. This is an obligation to the Promoter. The Contractor also has legal obligations to his employees, his sub-contractors, the Engineer and others.

Under the ICE conditions the Engineer has the duty and powers to see that the Contractor carries out his obligations under the contract. The obligation of the Engineer is therefore to use his powers so as to try to anticipate problems and be able to certify to the Promoter that the Contractor has carried out the contract.

Most of the clauses in the ICE conditions relate to the obligations of the Contractor and the powers of the Engineer. Important obligations of the Promoter include appointing the Engineer, making the site available, and paying the Contractor.

53

Satisfaction of the Engineer

ICE cl 13 states that the Contractor shall construct, complete and maintain the works in accordance with the contract to the satisfaction of the Engineer *and shall comply with the Engineer's instructions*. The Engineer can thus instruct the Contractor to satisfy him on any matter connected with the works.

Access to the works and all places whence materials, etc. are being obtained is the right of the Engineer and any person authorised by him, under ICE cl 37, and under cl 38 no work is to be covered up without the approval of the Engineer. By using his powers of consent under ICE cl 4 the Engineer should ensure that these rights of access and inspection are extended to any work by sub-contractors. The engineer and his representatives should therefore obtain the access they need to anticipate problems and give instructions to the Contractor.

Under ICE cl 66 the Promoter or the Contractor can refer any dispute or difference arising out of the contract to the Engineer for a decision, including any dispute about decisions, instructions, etc. by the Engineer. A dispute or difference must be referred to the Engineer for a decision before either party can refer it to arbitration.

Engineer's representatives

'Engineer's representative' is the title in the contract for a person appointed by the Promoter or the Engineer under ICE cl 1(d). The person may be the 'Resident Engineer' on site, or an assistant of the Engineer or a clerk of works, depending on the terms of the appointment. The appointment has to be notified to the Contractor in writing.

The functions of the Engineer's representative are defined in ICE cl 2(1) as watching and supervising construction. Cl 2(3) indicates that the Engineer's representative is responsible to the Engineer, though he may be appointed by the Promoter.

Under ICE cl 2(3) the Engineer can authorize his representative to exercise many of his powers related to supervision and instructions to the Contractor. The exceptions are powers on variations, extra time, disputes, certification of payments due to the Contractor and certification of completion.

The Engineer and his representative can appoint persons to assist them in supervision. Under ICE cl 2(4) the Contractor can refer back their instructions or acts which dissatisfy him.

Programme

The period for completing the work, and any other dates specified in a contract, are obvious obligations, mainly of the Contractor once he has been sent the Engineer's instruction to commence. Unless the contract states that these are only approximate periods or dates, what is known as 'time as the essence of a contract' applies and lateness in achieving a contract date is a breach of contract.

Once sent the instruction to commence under ICE cl 41, the Contractor is obliged to proceed with due expedition and without delay, but deciding the sequence, durations, methods and resources for the work and all it needs is the Contractor's responsibility (ICE cl 8). The Contractor is not relieved of any of his duties or responsibilities by the Engineer's approval of a programme and proposed methods (ICE cl 14(7)).

Requiring the Contractor to submit a programme and other information is the chief means available to the Engineer to try to be sure that the Contractor and his sub-contractors are likely to be able to complete the work satisfactorily by the contract dates. As suggested earlier, these powers need to be used as soon as a contract comes into effect. Time lost cannot be recovered. The Contractor can remove and replace work which is wrong in quality, location or dimensions. No-one can replace late work with early work.

The Contractor is not obliged to follow the programme approved by the Engineer. The value of requiring a programme to be submitted for approval is that the Engineer and his representatives can judge whether dates can be achieved and to indicate what the Contractor intends to do if he claims to have been delayed.

Regular meetings between representatives of the Engineer and the Contractor are the common means of reviewing progress and discussing remedies for problems. Meetings can be valuable for these purposes, for checking whether there is agreement on facts and for defining needs for actions. At the start of a contract the Engineer should establish by written agreement with the Promoter and the Contractor whether the records of meetings are not to be taken as committing any party or whether statements and decisions recorded in agreed minutes are to be taken as communications and instructions under the contract. If the latter is chosen, the statements and decisions need to be written with reference to the relevant clauses of the contract.

Discussion and advice to the Contractor are usual when the

Engineer or his representatives consider that the progress of work is too slow. Under ICE cl 46 the Contractor can be formally notified of this and is then obliged to take steps to expedite progress. If this fails, the Engineer and the Promoter can take action under ICE cl 63 (1)(d) to expel the Contractor.

Quality

The obligation of the Contractor to carry out work to the standards stated in the contract specification follows from his tender offer to do so.

Materials and workmanship are subject to the approval of the Engineer's representative (ICE cl 2). Failure to disapprove does not prejudice the power to disapprove subsequently (ICE cl 39). Removal and re-execution of materials or work not in accordance with the contract can be ordered, and if the Contractor fails to carry out such orders another can be employed to do it at his expense.

The above terms give great power to reject anything not satisfying the specification and the Engineer. Anticipation is preferable, not least to serve the Promoter's interest by avoiding delays. To do so the Engineer and his representatives can use the following powers:

- Assess the Contractor's proposed arrangements and methods of construction (ICE cl 14) to see if they should result in work of acceptable quality.

- Assess the Contractor's staff and employees for quality and performance, and use power under ICE cl 16 to require the Contractor to remove any for reasons of misconduct, incompetence or negligence.

- Examine and require tests of materials and workmanship, under ICE cl 36.

- Watch and supervise work early enough to foresee possible objections, with the powers under ICE cl 13 to instruct the Contractor where his work is not satisfactory and under ICE cl 8 if not adequate, stable or safe.

Construction safety

Under UK legislation the Promoter of a project, consultants, contractors and other employers are responsible for the health, safety and welfare of their employees at work and of any other person who may be affected. Employees and the self-employed also have duties to themselves and others.

The general duties of employers and individuals are stated in the Health & Safety at Work etc. Act, and specific requirements on sites in Construction Regulations. After 1992 different and probably more rules may be imposed by European Community directives. Under the present UK legislation the occurrence of accidents, or failures to have safety policies, systems and training, can be criminal matters. Self-regulation is intended, but the Factory Inspectorate and other statutory bodies have powers to inspect, order work to stop, close a site and to initiate prosecution.

In addition to the above requirements of the law, the Contractor enters into obligations to the Promoter under ICE cl 8(2) to take responsibility for the safety of site operations and under ICE cl 19 for the safety of persons on site, except work designed by or under the control of the Promoter or the Engineer. The Engineer as agent of the Promoter has the duty of seeing that the Contractor carries out these obligations. The Engineer and his representatives can do so by giving the Contractor general instructions under ICE cl 13 to carry out his safety obligations under the legislation, under cl 14 to require information on the safety of proposed methods of construction, under cl 15 to be satisfied that the Contractor's agent is capable of being responsible for safety, and under cl 4 to submit the appropriate extent of such information from a prospective sub-contractor before consenting to sub-letting.

In deciding the information to be submitted by the Contractor under ICE cl 14, the Engineer should consider what is relevant to the safety of individuals and the works, and also the Promoter's interests of avoiding claims and delays to construction because of accidents or disputes about safety. The Engineer and his representatives should also consider their own liabilities for negligence if they fail to watch and supervise all the Contractor's activities or fail to use their powers, for instance by not asking for sufficient detail, not checking it, or not foreseeing risks that a professional engineer should foresee.

Powers that can be used by the Engineer or his representatives include requiring the Contractor (and through him any sub-contractor) to remove an employee for misconduct or negligence

(ICE cl 16), suspending work for default (cl 40(1)(b)), and omitting payment because of dissatisfaction with work done, goods, materials or services (cl 60(7)). More positively, they can be prepared to use these powers and state this early in discussions so as to encourage all concerned to avoid safety problems.

The Contractor could object to a nominated sub-contractor (under ICE cl 59A (1)) for reasons of safety.

Bibliography

Supervision of construction, proceedings of conference, Thomas Telford Ltd, London, 1984.

Ninos G.E. and Wearne S.H., *Control of projects during construction*, report TMR 17, Technological Management, University of Bradford, 1984.

Managing health and safety in construction: Principles and application to main contractor/sub-contractor projects, Health & Safety Commission, HMSO, London, 1987.

Professional engineers at risk, seminar, Institution of Civil Engineers, London, 1988.

Arbitration Procedure, Institution of Civil Engineers, London, 1983.

11 Progress

Time is money is a phrase which summarizes the concern of all or most parties to a project that it should be completed as planned. Delays due to exceptional weather and other circumstances are a common risk in civil engineering. The Contractor may be entitled to extra time if his work is affected by some circumstances beyond his control, but otherwise may be liable to pay the Promoter damages for being late beyond the contract time for completion.

Extension of time

The Contractor may be entitled to extra time under the following clauses in the ICE conditions:

- 7(3)   Failure or inability of the Engineer to issue drawings or instructions.

- 12(3)   Physical conditions or artificial obstructions.

- 13(3)   The Engineer's directions or instructions.

- 14(6)   Methods of construction.

- 27(6)   Variations in relation to public utilities, street works.

- 31(2)   Facilities for other contractors, authorities or other statutory bodies.

- 42(1)   Delay in possession of the site.

- 44(1)   Variations, increased quantities, exceptional adverse weather or other special circumstances.

Several of these clauses may be a basis for claiming extra time and extra payment, but an extension of time does not automatically follow from a decision that extra payment is due, nor vice versa.

Under ICE cl 44(1) a claim from the Contractor for extra time is to be delivered to the Engineer within 28 days after the cause of the delay or as soon thereafter as is reasonable, with full and detailed particulars.

The Engineer makes the decision on the extension of time (if any) to which he considers the Contractor is entitled. The Engineer may grant an extension in the absence of any such claim.

Amount of extension

The amount of delay caused by some of the events that can be the basis of claims under the contract may be quite clear, for instance delay in possession of the site. Others may require detailed discussion between representatives of the Engineer and the Contractor. A decision by the Engineer should be based upon the facts, starting from the particulars (if any) from the Contractor, the programme of work approved under cl 14, and the site records of progress and of any related events.

At the due or extended date for completion and upon issuing the certificate of completion (ICE cl 48) the Engineer is obliged to review all the circumstances of a delay and may finally grant a longer extension of time.

Special circumstances

Under ICE cl 44 the Engineer can grant an extension of time for ' . . . special circumstances of any kind whatsoever which . . . fairly entitle the Contractor to an extension . . . '. This clause is open to a wide range of interpretations. In effect the Engineer may grant an extension of time for any reason he considers is justified. The Engineer thus has the equivalent of power to grant extra time *ex gratia* (out of thanks), for instance if the Contractor diverts resources from planned work in anticipation of some risk which could seriously disrupt or damage the works but does not in fact do so, though the Engineer cannot certify that the Promoter shall pay the Contractor's extra costs for this unless payable under a clause of the contract.

As other decisions by the Engineer, the Promoter can under ICE cl 66 dispute the reasons and the amount of extra time granted to the Contractor.

Damages for lateness

Under ICE cl 47 the Contractor is liable to pay the Promoter liquidated damages for delay in completing the works or a section of the works that has a separate completion date specified in the contract. The amount payable is a rate per day or week that should have been inserted in the appendix to the form of tender, and delay is relative to any extension of time granted under cl 44.

Payment of liquidated damages may not be the limit of the Contractor's liability for lateness, depending upon what is agreed in the contract.

As indicated, it is the Engineer who can grant extensions of time and he certifies when work is complete, but he has no discretion under the contract to vary or waive the amounts payable as liquidated damages.

Bibliography

Barnes N.M.L., Prevention is better than dispute, *International Construction Law Review*, July 1987, **4**, 3, 196—201.

12 Payment

Payment on time is important to the Contractor as the cost to him of credit to finance expenditure on people, plant and sub-contractors can be one of his biggest costs. Certifying payment due and making payment on time are important to the Engineer and the Promoter to avoid being in breach of contract.

Monthly payment

Payment under the ICE conditions is normally monthly and under ICE cl 56 based upon the remeasurement principle of quantities of work completed and their **value** for payment purposes in terms of quantities and rates in the BoQ.

Under ICE cl 60(1) the process of payment is initiated after the end of each month by a statement from the Contractor to the Engineer showing the estimated value of permanent work executed and any other amounts the Contractor considers he is entitled to — such as for goods or materials delivered to site, if payment for them is due under the contract.

The Engineer then has to certify the payment due in his opinion and the Promoter to pay. Under ICE cl 60(2) certification and payment have to be completed within 28 days of delivery of a statement from the Contractor to the Engineer or his representative.

Under ICE cl 60(4) up to 5 per cent of the certified value of amounts due to be paid to the Contractor each month is 'retained', i.e. not paid at that time. Part of this retention money is released when the Engineer certifies the substantial completion of the works, and the remainder after the end of the maintenance period.

If the value of work during a month is less than an amount stated in the appendix to the tender the Engineer is not bound to issue a certificate for its payment. It therefore accumulates for the next month.

Final account

Settlement of the total payment to the Contractor is initiated by a final account and supporting documentation due from him not later than 3 months after the end of the 'period of maintenance' (see chapter 14).

Within 3 months of receiving the information he requires for this the Engineer is obliged to issue a final certificate stating the amount he considers the Contractor is finally due. The balance of amount due is then to be paid within 28 days — it can be payment *to* the Promoter from the Contractor, for instance if amounts are due to the Promoter for defaults of the Contractor such as lateness under ICE cl 47(1) or for damage to a highway or bridge under ICE cl 30(3).

Late payment

Under ICE cl 60(6) interest is added to late payments of monthly or final amounts due to the Contractor.

Contract price adjustment

As stated earlier, the invitation for tenders for a contract should state if its terms are to include the clause headed 'Contract Price Fluctuations' published with the ICE conditions.

If this clause is included the amounts due in the monthly and final payments have to be increased or decreased in accordance with the method stated in the clause and applying the factors inserted in a copy of it issued with the invitation for tenders. The Contractor should show his calculations of the increases or decreases in his statement to the Engineer under ICE cl 60 and the Engineer or an assistant check these, as with all of a statement, in order to certify to the Promoter the payment due.

Claims

Each statement by the Contractor under ICE cl 60 could be called a claim of payment due, but here normal practice in the industry in the UK is followed, using the word 'claim' to mean an exceptional request, such as for payment not based upon progress in completing quantities of work or other items listed in the BoQ.

Claims for additional payment, time or any other change should therefore arise only because of unexpected or changed circumstances. Instructions to the Contractor to carry out his obligations under the contract should be given under cl 13 and thus not be a basis for claims.

- The Contractor may make such claims for additional payment under the following clauses in the ICE conditions:

o 5	Adjustment of contract documents because of ambiguities or discrepancies
o 7(3)	Failure or inability of the Engineer to issue drawings or instructions
o 12	Physical conditions or artificial obstructions
o 13(3)	The Engineer's directions or instructions
o 14(6)	Methods of construction
o 17	Errors in setting out based upon incorrect data supplied in writing by the Engineer or his representative
o 20	Excepted risks
o 26	Fees payable under legislation, rates and related taxation
o 27(6)	Variations in relation to public utilities, street works
o 31	Facilities for other contractors, authorities or other statutory bodies
o 32	Precautions to prevent removal or damage to things of geological or archaeological interest
o 36	Samples or tests not intended by or provided for in the contract
o 38	Uncovering and reinstating parts of the works
o 40	Suspension of the works ordered by the Engineer
o 42	Delay in possession of the site
o 49	Repairs to work not due to neglect or failure on the part of the Contractor
o 50	Some searches, tests or trials
o 52	Variations ordered by the Engineer
o 59A(3)	Loss, expense or damage arising from nomination of a sub-contractor

o 59B(4)   Termination of a nominated sub-contractor

o 63   Work done and value of plant etc. at time of expulsion of the contractor

o 64   Frustration of the contract

o 65   War

o 69   Tax fluctuations

o 70   Value added tax

o 71   Metrication

o *Optional clause*   Contract price fluctuation.

The clauses define the events which must occur for there to be a basis for a claim. ICE cl 52(4) states the procedure for making a claim, particularly the needs to submit within a time limit and to substantiate statements of costs and losses.

The Engineer has no power to accept a claim not made under a clause of the contract and not submitted as required by the relevant clause. He can recommend to the Promoter that a payment be made to the Contractor not under a clause of the contract *ex gratia*, for instance to pay for special effort by the Contractor in circumstances not envisaged in the contract.

The other model conditions of contract mentioned in chapter 5 give a contractor less reasons for being able to claim, and also less power to the Engineer or equivalent to accept them.

Engineer and auditors

Under the ICE conditions the Engineer has the powers to certify payments due to the Contractor and to make various decisions such as accepting claims, and ordering variations that affect costs to the Promoter. The Engineer has the power and the duty to decide if a claim has a valid basis and if valid, to certify the amount to be paid by the Promoter.

Within promoters' organizations these powers of the Engineer and his duty under a contract to use them may appear to be inconsistent with the role and authority of financial auditors. To avoid any such problems the Institution of Civil Engineers and the Chartered Institute of Public Finance and Accountancy have agreed the joint statement reproduced in Appendix E which establishes that the role of the auditors is that of reviewing the systems within a promoter's organization under which a person named as the Engineer for a contract makes his decisions, but not to interfere with the decisions of the Engineer or his representatives.

Bibliography

Armstrong W.E.I., *Contractual claims under the ICE conditions of contract*, 3rd ed, Chartered Institute of Building, London, 1987.

Engineers and auditors, undated, joint statement, Institution of Civil Engineers and the Chartered Institute of Public Finance & Accountancy (Reproduced in Appendix E).

13   Variations

Variations to the scope or programme of construction may be needed after agreeing a contract in order to respond to economic or other changes that affect the objectives of a project or in order to overcome problems of its design, site conditions or methods of construction.

Variation orders

Under ICE cl 51(1) the Engineer can order the Contractor to vary the works, within limits. The clause gives the Engineer power to order any variation in his opinion desirable for the satisfactory completion and functioning of the works. The clause also states that the Engineer shall order any variation in his opinion necessary for the completion of the works. In the latter circumstances he is obliged to order a variation, but he has the discretion whether to order a variation in his opinion desirable for satisfactory completion and functioning of the works.

The variations which the Engineer considers desirable he can therefore order if the Promoter wishes. Those he considers necessary under the wording of the clause he must order — an example of his role as a servant of the contract.

The Contractor is not allowed to make any variation without an order by the Engineer, but the clause does not prevent the Contractor proposing changes to the Engineer.

The clause defines variations very broadly, as including additions, omissions, substitutions, changes in quality, form, position or in sequence, method or timing of construction, but not changes in only the quantities of work.

Payment

Under ICE cl 52 the Engineer decides the payment for variations, after consultation with the Contractor. The clause in effect states that rates and prices in the BoQ should be used as far as relevant.

Failing agreement with the Contractor, the Engineer has the power to fix new rates or prices (called **star** items) for varied work. The Contractor can make a claim for a higher rate or price. Under ICE cl 52(4) the Contractor is obliged to keep records as may be necessary to support a claim. The Contractor is entitled to interim payment for as much as the Engineer considers is due.

The Engineer can order the Contractor to execute additional or substituted work on a dayworks basis, under ICE cl 52(3). The clause does not permit the dayworks basis of payment to be used for variations only in the form, position, sequence, method or timing of work.

Changes only in quantities are paid for by remeasurement.

Limitations on variations

The limits to the power of the Engineer to order variations are set by the words 'necessary' and 'desirable' in ICE cl 51. No limit is stated to the number or the costs of variations.

Whether the Promoter can afford or is willing to pay the cost can be a limitation on ordering a variation defined by the Engineer as desirable. The Promoter has no choice on a variation defined by the Engineer as necessary.

There is no authority in the ICE conditions for the Engineer to order variations to suit the wishes of the parties or the Engineer. They have to be necessary or desirable in the opinion of the Engineer and under the terms of the clause.

The Engineer has no power to vary the contract. He could be authorised by the Promoter to be his agent to negotiate changes with the Contractor, or both parties could agree to extend the Engineer's powers beyond those in ICE cl 51.

Other model conditions

The other model conditions listed in chapter 5 differ considerably from the ICE conditions in many of their terms. The FIDIC conditions are similar to the ICE conditions as regards variations, but have the addition that the Engineer may add or deduct an amount for the Contractor's site and overhead costs if the total value of variations ordered and remeasurement change the contract price by more than a stated percentage (FIDIC cl 52.3).

The GC/Works/1 conditions give the Superintending Officer the power to issue instructions for variations or modifications without limitation as to reasons or cost.

The IMechE/IEE/ACE and the IChemE 'Red Book' conditions give the Engineer the power to order variations, but limit the total cost of variations to a percentage of the contract price, not by reasons for a variation.

14 Handing over

What is usually called handing over or taking over the works can be complicated by the different interests of Promoter and Contractor in whether all or parts are substantially complete, tests have been passed, any work is outstanding and whether the Promoter is ready to use or has accepted or used part or all of the works.

Certificate of completion

Whether the works or sections are substantially complete is decided by the Engineer under ICE cl 48. His decision is given in a 'certificate of completion'. This states the date in the Engineer's opinion when the works were substantially completed. The certificate is issued to the Contractor and copied to the Promoter.

The date stated is the start of the 'period of maintenance'. The Contractor is liable in this period to remedy defects in the works, but 14 days after the issue of the certificate of completion his responsibilities for the care and the insurance of the works cease or are greatly reduced and he becomes entitled to some of the retention money.

The Contractor may request the issue of the certificate when he considers that the works have been substantially completed and have passed any final test prescribed in the contract. The notice making this request must be accompanied by an undertaking to finish any outstanding work in the period of maintenance.

Under ICE cl 48(1) the Engineer is bound to respond within 21 days to a request from the Contractor for a certificate, either by issuing it or by issuing instructions specifying work which he requires to be done first.

When and if he issues a certificate the Engineer does not have to specify the outstanding work to be finished by the Contractor in the period of maintenance. If the Engineer chooses to specify this he should consider including a note that only the work known to the Engineer to be outstanding is listed and this is not to be taken as the limit of the Contractor's liabilities.

Sectional completion

Under ICE cl 48(2) a certificate may be issued for a section of the works, similarly as above. This can be for a section of the works that had a separate time for completion stated in the appendix to the tender or for any substantial part of the works occupied or used by the Promoter.

No definition of substantial completion appears in the ICE conditions. It is made dependent upon the opinion of the Engineer, but the fact that a certificate may be issued because the Promoter has used part of the works indicates that substantial completion means fit to use (See Appendix C).

Care and insurance of the works

Under ICE cl 20 the Contractor ceases to be responsible for the care of the works or a section of the works 14 days after the issue of a certificate of completion, except for the outstanding work until it is complete.

Under ICE cl 21 the Contractor is responsible for the insurance of the works and his plant up to the above times and also during the period of maintenance from causes occurring prior to then or occasioned by the Contractor during the period of maintenance.

The 14 days is for giving the Promoter time to arrange his own insurance.

Period of maintenance

During what is called in ICE cl 49 the 'period of maintenance' the Contractor is responsible for finishing the work outstanding at the date of completion certified under cl 48 *and* for maintaining the works in the condition required by the contract, but fair wear and tear excepted. The clause defines his 'maintenance' obligations as being work of repair, amendment, reconstruction, rectification and making good defects, imperfections, shrinkages or other faults required by the Engineer during the period or within 14 days of its expiration. If the Contractor has failed to do any such work as required by the Engineer the Promoter can employ

71

others to do it and recover the cost from the Contractor.

The purpose of the period of maintenance is to give time after construction for defects to become apparent and be put right by the Contractor while he is still available. It is not a service for maintenance in the normal sense of remedying the effects of wear and tear.

The clause indicates that the intent is that the works shall become the Promoter's entire responsibility after the end of the period of maintenance, but it says that this may be 'as soon as practicable' after that time and it allows for the Contractor to finish outstanding work after that time.

Release of retention money

Payment of the retention money to the Contractor is in two stages.

Under cl 60(5) the issue of a certificate of completion should be followed within 14 days by payment to the Contractor of up to 1.5 per cent of the total payment due for the completion of the works. The clause includes provision for part-payment for sections of work certified as complete.

Payment of the remainder of the retention is due within 14 days of the end of the period of maintenance, but the Promoter can withhold amounts which in the opinion of the Engineer represent the cost of works remaining to be executed by the Contractor.

Taking over

The ICE conditions do not say that the Promoter takes over the works as they cease to be the responsibility of the Contractor. This is implied, and it is common sense that the Promoter or someone on his behalf should do so. The Engineer has the duty of issuing the certificate of completion if in his opinion it is due under the contract. As adviser the Engineer should therefore warn the Promoter before this that the Contractor will cease to be responsible for the care and insurance of the works and that he should be prepared to take over these responsibilities.

The IMechE and IChemE model conditions include provisions for the issue of taking over certificates. Their examples can be used in drafting taking over terms for contracts for equipment, systems and services for buildings.

15 Final comments

'Sure I've read it right through, parts of it'
— *attributed to Sam Goldwyn*

As said at the start of this Guide, contracts should be a means to an end. They should help to get projects constructed. To do this every contract for construction needs to be planned to suit the objectives, size and risks of the work. Part I of the Guide has therefore been a brief review of choices in the number of contracts, responsibilities, terms of payment and the scope of documents. Part II has been an indication of general terms available in the ICE model conditions of contracts for construction.

Part II has been based upon the ICE conditions as these are probably the most influential model in Britain and are related to the FIDIC model drafted for international use. General conditions of contract are not exciting reading, and not easily absorbed. The introduction to the ICE conditions in this Guide is intended to help by showing how the clauses define responsibilities and establish procedures for dealing with problems. What can be the most important clauses have been referred to. All the clauses need to be read in order to study their wording and to appreciate their possible effects as a whole.

The ICE conditions are longer than most of the alternatives mentioned. It is possible that the provisions they include for extensions of time, variations, nomination of sub-contractors, retention money and payment based upon a bill of quantities may lead to some problems, because the more detailed the terms of a contract the more scope for ambiguity or argument. This is particularly likely when events involve two or more of these terms of a contract. The clauses which define the obligations to construct and to pay are obviously needed. Other clauses could be considered as options, to be included if relevant and if worth the complication.

One intention of model conditions has been to produce predictable results from contracts. An instance is the idea of including terms for the payment of liquidated damages for a breach of contract. Such terms can produce more certain and quicker compensation if there is a clear breach, but in practice the typical example of the liability of a contractor to pay a fixed amount if late may become uncertain because it is complicated by other events that occur such as an excepted risk or a variation. The deterrent effect intended may also not be influential because a contractor can calculate his options. A contract without such prior agreements could therefore be more effective because the costs of breaching it are left uncertain, and it would be simpler. A contractor might also be more motivated to perform satisfactorily in order to be considered for further work.

Because a risk can be foreseen it is not necessarily best therefore for a contract to include a solution to its possible effects. What is important is considering this choice about all likely risks prior to commitment to a contract. The ICE conditions have been developed to incorporate many provisions which may be valuable, but they should not be thought to be a substitute for defining the objectives of a project, assessing its risks, deciding priorities between quality, cost and time, finalizing the drawings, selecting competent and motivated contractors, and authorizing one person to make decisions on any consequent problems.

Appendix A. **Abbreviations**

The following abbreviations are used in publications on British and some international engineering and construction contracts.

ACE	Association of Consulting Engineers
BEAMA	British Electrotechnical and Allied Manufacturers Association
BoQ	Bills of quantities
BAQ	Bills of approximate quantities
BEC	Building Employers' Confederation
BS	British Standard
CASEC	Committee of Associations of Specialist Engineering Contractors
CCPI	Committee for Coordinated Project Information (RIBA, RICS, BEC and ACE)
CCSJC	Conditions of Contract Standing Joint Committee (representing the ICE, ACE and FCEC)
CESMM	Civil Engineering Standard Method of Measurement (for a BoQ)
CIPFA	Chartered Institute of Public Finance and Accountancy
CIRIA	Construction Industry Research & Information Association
CPA	Contract price adjustment of tendered rates or prices to allow or partly allow for escalation — changes in material, labour or other costs during a contract*
EC	The European Community
ECE	United Nations Economic Commission for Europe
EEF	Engineering Employers Federation
FASSC	Federation of Associations of Specialists and Sub-Contractors

* Confusingly CPA is also used in network planning to mean critical path analysis.

FCEC	Federation of Civil Engineering Contractors
FIDIC	Fédération Internationale des Ingénieurs-Conseils (Lausanne)
ICE	Institution of Civil Engineers
IChemE	Institution of Chemical Engineers
IMechE	Institution of Mechanical Engineers
IEE	Institution of Electrical Engineers
ITT	Instructions to tenderers
JCT	Joint Contracts Tribunal for the Building Industry (representing the RIBA and other building industry organizations)
NECEA	National Engineering Contractors Employers Association
NEDO	National Economic Development Office
OCPCA	Oil and Chemical Plant Contractors Association
OED	Oxford English Dictionary
PCA	Price cost adjustment, as CPA
PIT	Progressing, inspection and testing
PSA	Property Services Agency
QA	Quality assurance
QS	Quantity Surveyor
RE	Resident Engineer (on site)
RIBA	Royal Institute of British Architects
RICS	Royal Institute of Chartered Surveyors
SMM	Standard method of measurement, as used in construction for measuring work when preparing a BoQ
SO	Supervising Officer or Superintending Officer
TQ	Technical query
VO	Variation order

Appendix B. **Definitions**

'And the Lord said ... confound their language, that
they may not understand one another's speech.'
— *Genesis ch XI*

*Model conditions of contract usually start with a clause defining some words
used. The definitions vary from contract to contract. In each case it is the meanings defined in that contract which apply. In this Guide the most typical or
most accurate meanings have been used. In this appendix are listed all that
may be doubtful or unfamiliar.*

   *Defined words are indicated in some contracts by starting them with capital
letters, but doing this or failing to do so has no significance under English law.*

Adhesive or **adherent** terms of contract means that the party proposing
   them does not intend to consider any alternatives. Also known as **boiler
   plate** terms.
Admeasurement — see **remeasurement**.
Agent — in general, anyone authorized to act for another person. In civil
   engineering in the UK it traditionally means a contractor's chief
   representative on a site and therefore the person who can commit that
   contractor by his/her agreements with another party.
The **Architect** — see the **Engineer**.
The **Authority** — see the **Promoter**.
Battle of the forms — a process of offer, counter-offer, counter-offer,
   etc. of proposals for conditions of contract, often consisting of
   exchanges of printed forms which have conditions of contract or terms
   of sale printed on their reverse side.
Bid = tender = offer.
Boiler plate terms — see **adhesive**.
Bond — see **guarantee**.
Breach — see *Appendix C*.
Clause — a paragraph or set of paragraphs in conditions of contract. A
   clause in this sense may contain several sentences. Each clause is usually
   numbered for reference. The scope of each clause is usually indicated

by a marginal note or heading, but one clause usually states that these notes or headings are included only to indicate the subject of the clauses and are not to affect their interpretation.

Compliant is used to mean that a tender meets or is required to meet all the terms of an invitation to tender.

Conditions of contract are strictly speaking all the terms of a contract which are fundamental to the intentions of the parties, so that failure to comply with a condition is breach of contract, but in this Guide the practice in the Engineering and other industries of calling documents 'conditions of contract' which are sets of clauses comprising conditions and warranties is followed.

Consideration — valuable consideration means payment.

Consortium — an organization formed by two or more established organizations for the purpose of one or more projects or contracts.

Contract price adjustment or fluctuation (CPA) — changes in contract price to compensate for changes in national or regional wage rates and material costs.

Contract — under English law, an agreement enforceable by law.

Contract price — should be used to mean the total amount to be paid a contractor for performance, as distinct from what it cost the contractor. The value of the work performed may be different from its cost or price, but in civil engineering in the UK the word **valuation** is used to mean the process of calculating the amount of payment due under a contract. **Fixed price** usually means that a tender total will not be subject to escalation, but it may mean that there is no variations clause. Like other words used in the industry, 'fixed price' has no fixed meaning. What matters in each contract are the terms of that contract. **Firm price** also varies in its meaning, but is often used to indicate that a tendered price is offered only for a stated period and is not a commitment if not accepted within that period.

The **Contractor** — the contractor named in a contract, as distinct from any contractor. The word 'the' is important in English practice as identifying the particular contractor. In some other countries where the English language is used in contracts the practice is to write "Contractor" or <Contractor> to indicate the one named. The contractor may be a **joint venture** or a **consortium** of two or more firms.

Construction — the physical activities of using materials, machines and labour to construct a building, structure, etc., and also usually including obtaining these and planning how to use them. To a lawyer the **construction** of a contract means not only using words to form a contract; it also means construing the terms, that is interpreting and explaining the agreement.

Cost — see **contract price.**

Damages — compensation for loss — see *Appendix C.*

Dayworks — usually construction work done by a contractor as instructed and to be paid for by the employer on the basis of hourly rates per hour for labour or plant. This is a particular form of reimbursable terms of payment. A section for dayworks rates is usually a part of a bill of quantities when sent out as one of the documents for inviting tenders.

Determination of a contract — termination, by completion of all obligations, or by agreement, frustration or breach — see *Appendix C.*

Direct labour — a promoter's own employees employed on construction, sometimes under internal contracts, otherwise as a service department.

Direct works — construction by direct labour.

Discharge of a contract — see *Appendix C.*

Domestic sub-contractor — see **sub-contractor.**

Duties under a contract — obligations.

Employer — an organization or person employing any other organization or person. Used in the ICE and the FIDIC conditions of contract to mean a **promoter** when employing a contractor.

The **Engineer** — the person named to exercise powers and duties under a contract. Equivalents in some construction contracts are 'the Architect', 'the Superintending Officer' or 'the Supervising Officer', but with powers and duties varying from contract to contract.

Enquiry — invitation for tenders.

Equipment — see **plant.**

Escalation — sometimes used to mean all exceptional or unexpected changes in costs.

— sometimes used to mean changes in the cost of the works due to rises or falls in national or regional wage rates or materials costs. See also **contract price adjustment.**

Excepted risks — events which may entitle a contractor or sub-contractor to extra time or payment.

Express — stated in a contract, i.e. expressed.

Firm price — see **contract price.**

Fixed price — see **contract price.**

Force majeure — an overwhelming event, such as war.

General contractor — a firm which works as a main contractor.

Guarantee — in finance and insurance circles a guarantee means an undertaking by a third party to recompense a party to a contract for a specified fault by the other party — see the companion Guide *Civil engineering insurance and bonding* by Peter Madge.

— in engineering a guarantee can mean a warranty from a seller to a buyer of the performance of a system, equipment or whatever.

House contractor — a contractor regularly employed by a promoter.

Implied terms — see *Appendix C*.

Joint venture — two or more organizations acting as one for a particular project or contract.

Liquidated damages — An amount agreed as compensation for loss or potential loss, usually stated in a contract in anticipation of a possible need to agree compensation.

Main contractor — one taking on the construction of all or nearly all a project (but usually employing sub-contractors).

Maintenance period — in some UK contracts meaning a period for a contractor to remedy defects — see **retention.**

Making a contract — entering into a contract. The agreement may include a term that the contract does not come into effect until some later date or action, or that the work is not to start until the contractor is instructed to do so.

Management contractor — a contractor employed by the employer to plan, define and perhaps supervise work to be carried out by other contractors.

Managing contractor — can mean a main contractor or a management contractor.

Measure and value — see **remeasurement.**

Measurement — calculation of quantities for a BoQ.

Model conditions of contract — sets of clauses and forms of agreement drafted for use in a sector of industry or for a type of project, often also called model forms. The 'ICE contract' is an example of a model form agreed by various interested organizations, in this instance by representatives of the ICE, consulting engineers and contractors — see *chapter 5.*

Nominated — see **sub-contractor.**

Open tendering — any interested contractor can tender — see **selective tendering.**

Order = contract.

Parties are the persons who offer and accept the terms of a contract. (A company or corporation has legally the status of a person). **Third parties** are any others who are not parties to a contract but who may have rights under its terms.

Performance of a contract is the completion of all the obligations of all the parties.

Plant — in some contracts defined as the goods, machinery, etc. to be supplied and erected by a contractor. In other contracts the plant or the equipment is defined as the machinery, etc. owned or hired by the contractor in order to carry out the works.

Pre-qualification — selection of contractors before inviting their tenders for a contract — see **selective tendering.**

Price — see **contract price.**

Prime cost item — see *chapter 3.*

Privity — the private relationship or mutual interest of parties to a contract.

The **promoter** — the client, owner, employer or buyer in different model forms of contract agreed for engineering and construction projects. The Institution of Civil Engineers uses ' the Promoter' up to the making of a contract, and 'the Employer' in its model form of contract. The promoter may be a contractor, for instance if investing in constructing a building for subsequent sale. The promoter may be a joint venture or consortium of two or more organizations.

Provisional sum — see *chapter 3.*

Qualified acceptance — a limited, modified or restricted acceptance of an offer, and therefore a counter offer, not an acceptance.

Qualified tender — a limited, modified or restricted offer, not compliant with all the terms proposed in an invitation for tenders.

Quantum meruit — literally the amount he, she or it deserves, meaning a reasonable price.

Rate — price per unit quantity of an item.

Remeasurement — calculation of the actual quantities of work completed by a contractor under a BoQ contract and hence the payment due. Also known as admeasurement or measure-and-value.

Remoteness — not being a party to a contract, i.e. no privity.

Resident engineer — the usual title in civil engineering in the UK for the engineer's representative on site, but depending upon the delegation of powers under the contract by the Engineer. In mechanical and electrical construction a contractor's chief engineer on a site may have the title 'Resident Engineer'.

Retention — retention money — a part of payment to a contractor which is not paid until he has discharged liabilities to remedy defects for a period after the taking over or acceptance of the works. In the ICE conditions this period is called the period of maintenance, and is typically 12 months.

Selective tendering — inviting tenders only from selected contractors, usually contractors already qualified by their performance of previous contracts and assessed as having sufficient resources.

Star items — rates or prices in a BoQ decided by the Engineer for work under a variation order.

Serial contract — one contract agreed for the construction of a series of projects or separate instalments of work. See also **term contract.**

Sub-contractor — a contractor employed by the main contractor and not in contract with the Promoter. A **nominated** sub-contractor is one nevertheless chosen by the Promoter or nominated by the Engineer. A **domestic** sub-contractor is one chosen by the main contractor.

Sub-letting — employment of a sub-contractor by a main contractor to undertake part of the works or provide services.

The **Superintending Officer** — see the **Engineer**.

The **Supervising Officer** — see the **Engineer**.

Tender — an offer to enter into a contract with a promoter.

Term contract — a contract for providing construction or other work when ordered by a promoter at any time within an agreed period (the 'term'), usually based upon descriptions of types of work which may be ordered but without quantities being known in advance. **Term** is not otherwise used here to mean a period of time, nor a particular word.

Terms of a contract are all the obligations and rights agreed between the parties, plus any terms implied by law. The terms may consist of conditions and warranties.

Terms of sale = conditions of contract. Terms of sale is more typically the phrase used for small contracts such as in purchasing materials.

Third parties — see **parties**.

Tort — see *Appendix C*.

Turnkey contract — not a precise description. What it means depends upon the terms of a contract, but typically a contract in which one contractor is responsible for the design, supply, construction and commissioning of a complete building, factory or process plant. In the USA 'turnkey' has been defined as meaning that the contractor is responsible for everything to complete a project excepting only things the contract says are the responsibility of its promoter.

Valuation — see **contract price**.

Variation — a change ordered by the Engineer under a clause of a contract.

Videmus — a comparison of tenders, particularly the rates and prices in BoQs, usually prepared for a report and recommendations on selecting a contractor.

The **work** — defined in CESMM2 as including work to be carried out, goods, materials and services to be supplied, and the liabilities, obligations and risks to be taken by a contractor.

Appendix C. **Legal notes**

'You always pay for free advice'

A little knowledge of the law is essential in contract management. A summary of some relevant legal principles is therefore given here, but as a summary can only indicate the nature of the rules, readers should not rely on any such secondary guidance and should take expert advice such as to be obtained in the books listed at the end of this appendix.

References to legal cases are given in square brackets.

Basis of English Law

Statute Law — made by Parliament but interpreted by the courts.

Common Law — This is essentially judge made law based on the Common Law rules and the principles of equity.

It is its Common Law which differentiates between English Law and that of Scotland and most continental countries which have systems based largely on Roman Law. Ireland and the USA also have Common Law systems.

EC Law — This is obviously the newest branch and is concerned mostly with harmonization of social systems and therefore equalisation of costs and of opportunities between the European Community states. Its Court of Justice gives judgements that are binding in all EC states.

Contracts

The law of contract is based on all the above. It governs the civil obligations and liabilities freely entered into between persons, legal persons or corporations.

Under English law a contract is not legally enforceable if:

● It has an illegal aim.

- It is prohibited by law, for instance if it:

o interferes with the administration of justice
o affects the safety of the State
o tends to injure social or economic well being (e.g. by restraint of trade)
o it is entered into under duress or as a result of undue influence or as a result of material misrepresentation
o it is made by a legally incompetent person, i.e. a minor or someone who is drunk or of unsound mind.

There are two types of agreement recognised as legally enforceable:

- *Simple contracts* — can be oral or written (or part of each) and depend on:

o offer
o acceptance (which must be outright — see below)
o valuable consideration (usually payment)
o identity of intention
o intention to make a legal relationship
o possibility.

- *Speciality contracts* — contracts under seal. These depend entirely on their form, i.e. being under seal, which of itself will show the intention to make a legal relationship, and need not include all the above six.

An advantage under English law of sealing is that the period for making claims for defects is extended to 12 years compared to 6 years, from the date of breach — see also *Appendix D*.

Requirements for a contract

In a simple contract:

- *Offer*: An offer has to be complete (usually specification, conditions, price, etc.) and must be directed to a particular person or company.

o Withdrawal of an offer is effective only when the other party knows.
o Acceptance of an offer is effective when issued by acceptor.
o Note the possibility of conflict if both are sent by post. If a period or date for acceptance is specified an offer will automatically lapse

unless specifically extended. If no period or date is specified it will lapse after a reasonable time.

- *Acceptance*: Unconditional acceptance binds both parties. A conditional acceptance is not in fact an acceptance but a counter offer and is equivalent to rejection of initial offer unless it is a condition or stipulation normally implied in law, e.g. under the Sale of Goods Act or Common Law (e.g. the duty to exercise skill and care).

- *Consideration*: Must be valuable consideration, usually payment. (This is not so in Roman Law countries).

- *Identity of intention*: Both parties must have a correct understanding as to the existence of the subject matter of the contract, and of one another's identity and promises under the contract and of its nature. Otherwise the contract will be void by mistake.

- *Intention to make a legal relationship*: The above imply the intention of the parties to make a legal relationship, but their inclusion of a clause denying such an intention will turn the deal from a binding contract into a 'gentlemen's agreement'.

Terms of contracts

These divide into:

- *Conditions*: terms so directly affecting the purpose of the contract that non-compliance with them amounts to a substantial failure to perform the contract as a whole.

- *Warranties*: an auxiliary stipulation in the nature of a guarantee which does not go to the root of the contract.

Thus many of what are called 'conditions of contract' are not in fact conditions but only warranties.

Breach of a condition entitles the other party to repudiate the contract although he can choose to treat it as a breach of warranty and sue for damages.

Whether a term of a contract is viewed by a court as a condition or as a warranty may depend upon the nature of a breach.

- *Implied terms*: These are terms which are part of a contract by law, not by the choice of the parties. They can include:

o   the duty to exercise skill and care (especially important in contract between a client and a professional engineer)
o   fitness for purpose (where the purpose has been made known to supplier and is not overridden by an imposed specification)
o   responsibility of a contractor for his sub-contractors
o   compliance with Construction Regulations, Factories Act, Health & Safety at Work etc. Act
o   furtherance of purpose — both parties will do their best to perform the contract
o   liability of a contractor to carry out his work at reasonable speed.

Terms such as fitness for purpose can be excluded from a contract by express agreement between the parties.

Actions on problems

The law provides means for action on three kinds of problems which can arise:

o   Breach of contract
o   Breach of trust
o   Tort (a breach of a duty).

Contract documents: Rules of interpretation

What is written is interpreted on the basis of that which the parties intended, which must be gathered from within the contract documents — not what might have been written or what was in a draft but excluded. The contract documents must be construed as a whole. Words that are clear and unambiguous will be preferred to any apparent general intention.

Ambiguities

An apparent or patent ambiguity is allowed to be explained by whatever evidence the contract documents provide or by external admissible evidence, but not evidence by the parties as to their intentions. A latent ambiguity (not apparent until you try to do what the document says and cannot) may be resolved by evidence as to intention.

Particular and general words

Where particular words which describe a category of persons or things are followed by general words then the general words will be confined to the same category. The rule is excluded where its application would not carry out the intentions of the parties.

Reasonableness

The standard of reasonableness expected of the Engineer is that of a reasonably competent engineer.

Substantial completion

Substantial completion is when the essentials necessary for the full accomplishment of the purpose of a contract have been completed [Worthington Corp. v Consolidated Aluminium Corp., 544F. 2d 227 (5th Cir. 1976)].

Completion or discharge of contract

A contract will be determined (terminated) by:

- *Completion*: performance of all their obligations by all parties wholly in accordance with the contract.

- *Discharge*: which can arise from agreement between the parties to terminate the contract.

- *Frustration*: where performance becomes impossible due to an unexpected supervening event which must be so unexpected as to be beyond the contemplation of the parties even as a possibility that neither party when contracting can be said to have accepted the risk of its taking place.

- *Fundamental breach* in performance (by either party): that is a breach going to the root of the agreement. In this case the innocent party can choose either to treat the matter as a repudiation by the other party, unless the innocent party has received a substantial benefit or property has passed to him, or as a breach of warranty only. In either case the innocent party can also claim damages.

Breach of contract

Breach can follow from failure to comply with any term of a contract. The most common are listed below.

Failure to comply with specification

Generally defects in compliance can be remedied, but wrong construction or the destruction of materials, etc. ('disconform performance') can make it impossible for the works as specified ever to be constructed. Failure to comply with the specification is likely to be a breach of warranty.

Delay in performance

Under common law time is taken to be 'of the essence' of a contract unless a contrary intention is clearly shown.

If no date or period for completion has been explicitly stated, a reasonable time will be inferred to be binding. Equitable considerations prevail and 'specific performance' (e.g. insistence that the works are completed) is required plus the payment of damages for delay.

Delays caused by an employer such as in giving access to the site, delivery of drawings, nomination of nominated sub-contractors or in giving instructions can be breaches by an employer.

If completion is rendered impossible because of a fault of his employer then a contractor will have a right to payment for the work actually done **quantum meruit** — not at the rates tendered.

Delay in payment

Interference by an employer in the issue by the Engineer of certificates or delay in making payments would be breach. A contractor is at liberty to treat this only as a breach of warranty and seek damages in compensation.

Conduct of the parties

This covers a great variety of matters dealt with in the conditions of contract, for instance if a contractor refuses to accept instructions, failure to take care for safety or to obey regulations.

Liquidated damages

In all cases where the act in question is a breach of contract, English law will require that the payment or forfeiture provided for in a contract is not a penalty ('in terrorem').

To be legally sustained the amount set for liquidated damages must be a genuine pre-estimate of the damages which could conceivably flow from the breach. A promoter should therefore keep a record of the calculations used as a basis for the amount stated in a liquidated damages clause.

If it is held to be a penalty, the party claiming it will not be permitted to recover the full amount if his damage has in fact been less, but on the other hand will not be limited to that amount if his damages have been greater.

There would be difficulties in the way of a party who had suffered greater damage arguing that a clause inserted for his benefit was in fact a penalty, though a clause which is not a genuine pre-estimate of damage may in some cases be a deliberate limitation imposed by the parties on the amount of possible damage rather than a penalty. If it is held to be liquidated damages, the aggrieved party will be entitled to the stipulated sum whether his real damage be greater, or less, or non-existent.

Decisions on whether to include a liquidated damages clause and, if so, a genuine estimate of the likely amount of damages should be agreed between a promoter and his advisers before the tender documents are prepared. The prospective Engineer should ensure that they understand the importance of the liquidated damages clause, the inclusiveness of the stipulated sum, and the likely interpretation by a Court in event of any dispute.

Limitation of contractual liability

The period of limitations is the time available to either party to take action for breach of contract. See *Appendix D* for a summary of the recent English legislation.

There is an obligation under ICE cl 13 and other model conditions for the works to be completed to the satisfaction of the Engineer *and* to fulfil all contractual obligations. The issue of a 'maintenance certificate' under ICE cl 48 signifies compliance with the first but not necessarily of the second.

Tort

Negligence

For there to be negligence there must be:

- a legal duty of care imposed by Common Law or Statute, e.g. Health and Safety at Work etc. Act, *and*

- a breach of that duty by failure to use reasonable care, *and*

- damage, not too remote, resulting from that breach.

Nuisance

This is defined as 'unlawful interference with a person's use or enjoyment of land, or of some right over, or in connection with it'.

'What would be a nuisance in Belgrave Square would not necessarily be so in Bermondsey'. [Thesiger L.J., Sturgess v Bridgman (1879)].

Particular duties and responsibilities of the Engineer towards the Promoter

The duties and responsibilities of the Engineer towards his employer depend upon the terms of his contract of service. The terms should cover the following.

Design

To provide a design which is skilful, effective within financial limits imposed by the Promoter and comprehensive. Normally 'it is sufficient if he exercises the ordinary skill of an ordinary competent man exercising that particular art'. [McNair H., Bolam v Friern Hospital Management Committee (1957)].

There is an implied warranty by an engineer who undertakes design that it will fit the purpose made known to him. 'It was the duty of the contractors to the building owners to see that the end product was reasonably fit for the purpose for which it was required. That was an absolute duty'. '. . . Greaves (the Contractor) found that they needed expert assistance . . . The way the work was done in the factory was made perfectly well known to Baynhams who were given the task of designing the floor by the composite construction. As it was a new system the British Standards Institution had issued a pamphlet which contained a note to which Baynhams should certainly have adhered "The designer should satisfy himself that no undesirable vibrations can be caused by the imposed loading" . . . there was a breach of a contractual duty to provide and supply a design which would produce a building capable of taking the stacker trucks without damage or danger'. [Lord Denning, MR, Greaves & Co. (Contractors) Ltd. v Baynham Meikle and Partners (1975)].

There is no implied right to delegate the duty of design and no implied authority for an architect to employ a sub-contractor, nominated or otherwise, to design the building. [Sir Walker Carter OR, Moresk v Hicks (1966)].

Examination of the site

The Engineer is not entitled to rely solely on information provided to him by the employer as to the nature of ground. [Moneypenny v Hartland

(1826)]. It was held by the High Court of Australia that as a matter of law a contractor may have a claim against an employer for the latter's negligence in compiling and furnishing site information, despite stringent terms in the contract requiring tenderers to inform themselves as to the site and local conditions and restricting their right to rely on information supplied by the Promoter. [Morrison Knudsen International Co. Inc. v Commonwealth of Australia (1972)].

Local authorities have been held liable to houseowners for the negligence of their surveyors in passing houses as complying with by-laws although the foundations were quite inadequate. [Dutton v Bognor Regis (1972), Sparham Souter and another v Town and Country Development and Benfleet Urban District Council (1976), and Pinns v London Borough of Merton (1977)].

Estimate of project cost

Where an architect's or engineer's estimate is shown by tenders to be excessively low then he is in breach of an implied term of his agreement and can be dismissed without recompense [Moneypenny v Hartland, (1826), Nelson v Spooner, (1861), Flannagan v Mate (1876)]. He can also be sued for damages arising from this negligence.

In a New Zealand case [Young v Cosgrove (1963)] a contractor was held liable for negligence to a promoter who entered into a contract with him for building work at an hourly rate on the faith of the contractor's negligent underestimate of the time it would take to do the job.

Recommending form of contract

An engineer has a responsibility for the appropriateness or deficiencies in the conditions of contract he recommends for use.

Recommending contractors

An engineer does not guarantee the solvency or capacity of a contractor but may have a duty to make reasonable inquiries thereon if he, rather than the promoter, is responsible directly or indirectly for selection of the contractor. [Heys v Tindal (1861)].

Preparation of bills of quantities and measurement

Reasonable accuracy is required, but mistakes will occur and are accepted. [London School Board v Northcroft (1889)].

Certification

The Engineer must exercise reasonable care and may be liable for damages suffered due to negligent certification. [Sutcliffe v Thackrah (1974)].

Particular duties and obligations of the Engineer (as the Promoter's agent) towards the Contractor

Disclosure of information at tender stage

A promoter was found liable for a contractor's damages resulting from the promoter's failure to disclose knowledge that his officials and agents possessed at the time of bidding. [Earl L. Reamer Co. v City of Swartz Creek, 256 N W 2d 447, Michigan Court of Appeals (1977)].

Delivery of drawings and instructions

Drawings necessary for the execution of the works are to be provided within a reasonable time of the obligation arising.

For original works the obligation arises at the date of contract, for variations at the date they are ordered [McAlpine v Transvaal Provincial Administration (1974)], but not necessarily in sufficient time for a contractor to execute and complete the work in an economic and expeditious manner and/or in sufficient time to prevent his being delayed in such execution and completion.

Reasonable time does not depend solely on the convenience and financial interests of a contractor: it must also be regarded from the point of view of the Engineer and will depend, inter alia, on the order in which the works are to be carried out as approved by the Engineer, whether the contractor has requested details, whether the details relate to original work or variations and to the length of the contract period etc. [Diplock J., Neodox Ltd v Swinton and Pendlebury B.C. (1958)].

A contract drawing detailing the replacement of an underground cable at a military installation in New Jersey contained two different scales. After a contractor estimated and bid the job using the wrong scale, he requested additional costs for performing the work in accordance with the correct scale. The court concluded: 'If a contractor enters into a contract aware of the fact of defective specifications, it is not entitled to recover a claim based on these defective specifications.' [Wickham Contracting v US, Court of Claims (15.12.76)].

APPENDIX C

Sub-contracts

Special requirements if a sub-contract includes design
Special precautions are necessary if a sub-contractor is required to include
for design services which otherwise would be performed by the Engineer.
In such instances the Engineer should first make the situation plain to,
and have it approved by his employer.

Representations made by a sub-contractor before the award of a sub-contract
Under English law written or oral representations given by sub-contractors
in order to induce the award of work to them are legally binding.

Nomination of a sub-contractor

*Preservation of correct Engineer/main contractor and main contractor/
sub-contractor relationships*
The Engineer is deemed to be acting as the main contractor's agent in
negotiating with and then nominating a sub-contractor. Thus, in any
consequent negotiations or correspondence with such a sub-contractor
the Engineer must ensure that the main contractor is not by-passed —
he must be given opportunity to send other representatives to meetings,
he must be sent copies of all correspondence etc., and his legal position
must at all times be guarded. Otherwise, a direct contract between the
sub-contractor and the Promoter may be created.

Compatibility with conditions of main contract
Under ICE cl 59 the Contractor cannot be required to employ a nominated
sub-contractor who does not:

- undertake towards him, in respect of the sub-contracted work, the
  same obligations and liabilities as the contractor is under towards
  the Promoter in respect of the work, and

- indemnify the Contractor against negligence and misuse by the
  sub-contractor's workmen.

The FCEC model form of sub-contract contains these requirements.
  If a nominated sub-contract is accepted on terms which are less onerous
than those of the main contract, and therefore presumably at a lower price

than otherwise, then the Promoter may well have to bear losses stemming from the failure of the sub-contractor to fulfil his obligations.

Particular responsibilities of the Engineer in respect of a nominated sub-contract
The Engineer must watch that he does not interfere with the timing of the main contract by failing to take necessary action in cases where defects arise.

If a nominated sub-contractor is unable to complete the work as a result of being in the hands of a receiver, the Engineer's duty is to nominate another.

In general the main contractor is to be treated as responsible for all nominated sub-contractors' shortcomings, but cl 12(1) in the FCEC model form of sub-contract lays down that the sub-contractor is not required to indemnify the main contractor if the latter is entitled to indemnity by the Promoter under the main contract.

Failure of a sub-contractor's work is held to be a failure by the main contractor and not one for which he is entitled to an extension of time. The exception to this rule has been where the conditions of the nominated sub-contract varied from those of the main contract.

Bibliography

Davis F.R., *Contract*, 5th edition, Sweet & Maxwell, London, 1986.

Uff J., *Construction law*, 4th ed., Sweet & Maxwell, London, 1985.

Duncan Wallace I.N., *Construction contracts: Principles and policies in tort and contract*, Sweet & Maxwell, London, 1986.

Myers J.J., When might a Contractor refuse to perform work ordered by an Employer?, *International Contract Law Review*, **4**, pt 3, July 1987, 155–171.

Appendix D.   Liability for latent damage

This appendix is based upon an Institution of Civil Engineers' note for members produced in 1988. The full note (ref. LAC/88/2) gives a summary of liabilities under contract, tort and statute, but only the sections related to statutory liability are reproduced here.

This note and the notes in Appendix E are used here with the permission of the Legal Affairs Committee of the Institution.

Introduction
In recent years, professional engineers, like architects, doctors, solicitors, accountants and other professional people, have become increasingly at risk through the bringing against them of actions for negligence. In the past, insurance has generally provided adequate protection, but this is now becoming unduly expensive and is sometimes difficult to obtain. Recently, an attempt was made by Parliament to rationalise this field of liability in the Latent Damage Act 1986.

The basis of liability
Under the law of England and Wales, professional liability can arise in general in three distinct ways, namely in contract, in tort or under some particular statute. Moreover, liability may arise in more than one way in respect of a single series of events, and may affect individuals personally as well as the consultants, contractors, public authorities or other organisations by which they are employed. Again, while the details may vary, similar precepts apply in other parts of the United Kingdom and, indeed, under nearly all foreign jurisdictions based on common law.

Liability under statute
Statutory liability has increased vastly in recent years. The supply of services is now subject to the Unfair Contract Terms Act 1977 and the

95

Supply of Goods and Services Act 1982, while both goods and services will shortly be subject to the provisions of the Consumer Protection Bill currently before Parliament, which will apply to the United Kingdom various European Commission directives on consumer's rights and product liability. In other fields the Occupiers Liability Acts, the Defective Premises Act and similar statutes lay down duties and standards closely affecting many professional people. Legislation on health and safety, building regulations and the like not only create or extend duties and fix standards but also bring criminal sanctions to their enforcement.

Alternative actions

Liability can arise in contract, in tort or under one or more statutes and one defendant can be liable to the same plaintiff under more than one of these heads. It used to be the law that a plaintiff intending to sue a defendant would have to choose to proceed in contract or in tort, but not both, and, if he chose wrongly and his action failed, he could not then sue again under the alternative head. However, a plaintiff can now sue in the alternative under any or all of the above heads at the same time and, the defendant can then join other potential defendants as third and fourth parties. Complex multi-party action is now common place, often leading to inordinate delay in obtaining judgment with attendant inflation of costs.

Limitation of actions

In almost all jurisdictions the time within which civil claims can be brought before the Courts has been restricted. The reason is simple; if trial of claims arising out of a given event is delayed too long the plaintiff suffers by being kept out of his lawful remedy, the defendant may have lost the evidence necessary to support any defence, and the Court is faced with serious problems when all the available evidence is stale. The remedy is to set a time limit beyond which the plaintiff is prevented from bringing his claim.

UK law prescribes different limitation periods for different kinds of action but, at least until 1963, each period started to run on the date of accrual of the right of action. This 'accrual date' also varied with the kind of action; thus, in actions for breach of contract, time began to run from the date of breach; and for torts such as negligence where damage must be proved, the accrual date was the date upon which the damage occurred. However, where the damage resulting from a negligent breach of duty was of a kind which could not immediately be discovered by the plaintiff — that is, where the damage was 'latent' — the limitation period could expire before the plaintiff could know that he had a right of action, which would therefore be lost.

For this reason the Limitation Act 1963 introduced, for cases involving personal injury, extensions of the limitation period to when the victims knew, or with reasonable diligence ought to have known, that damage had occurred. The principle of 'discoverability' was then gradually extended by the Courts to other kinds of action, but in 1983 the House of Lords in the *Pirelli* case ruled that in 'damage to property' actions the older date of occurrence of damage should be observed.

With regard to statutory liability, each statute lays down its own starting dates for the limitation periods. The time for actions under the Defective Premises Act 1972 runs from the date upon which the premises are completed, while for actions against local authorities the date is that upon which a dwelling poses a present or imminent danger to public health or safety.

A further complication arises from the 'joint tortfeasor' rule under which a plaintiff is free to sue any single defendant for the full value of his loss even where more than one party has caused or contributed to the damage and the defendant sued is only partly to blame. Claims by the party so sued for contribution from other culpable parties have always been an exception to the normal limitation periods and result, in effect, to an extension of those periods.

The length of the limitation period

Periods of limitation have always varied from case to case. Thus, in contract the period was six years (or twelve years in the case of a contract under seal), in tort it was six years and for personal injury it was three years. Bearing in mind that all limitation periods cease to run when a writ is issued, but that the writ need not be served immediately and remains valid until twelve months after it is issued, and that in some cases the Court has a discretion — albeit limited — to extend the validity of a writ, it has seldom been possible to identify with certainty when the risk of being sued would come to an end. In the case of latent damage, actions could in theory be brought against a defendant or his estate many years or even centuries after the events giving rise to the claim.

The Latent Damage Act 1986

The Limitation Act 1980 was largely the result of the Law Reform Committee's 21st Report in 1977 on the general law of limitation. The Committee's 24th Report on Latent Damage was presented to Parliament in November 1984 after wide consultation during which the Institution and the other construction bodies made a substantial contribution. In this Report the Committee concluded that the law as it then stood was unjust to plaintiffs and defendants and was in need of reform, but that such reform was bound to be a compromise between conflicting interests. It then went on to recommend that there should be no change in the law of accrual of actions, that in negligence cases involving latent defects the plaintiff should be allowed three years from the date of discovery or reasonable discovery of significant damage in which to bring his claim over and above the existing six-year limitation period, but that in such cases the plaintiff should normally be barred from initiating court action more than fifteen years from the defendant's breach of duty whether or not damage had by then occurred. After further consultations, a Bill was introduced into the House of Lords to implement virtually the whole of the Committee's recommendations as they stood.

The main effects of the Act may be summarised as follows:

(a) The existing law with regard to the date of accrual of actions and to limitation periods remains unaltered. Thus the basic principle that an action in negligence accrues on the date damage occurs is retained;

(b) In addition to the normal six-year limitation period a further three-year period is made available running from the date on which the plaintiff discovered or ought with reasonable diligence to have discovered that he has an action;

(c) Notwithstanding the foregoing six- and three-year periods, the plaintiff's action will now become statute-barred after the expiry of a fifteen-year 'long-stop' period running from the date of the defendant's breach of duty;

(d) However, neither the 'long-stop' period nor any other limitation period will operate where there has been fraud, mistake or deliberate concealment of material facts by the defendant. It may also be suspended in respect of any period during which the plaintiff is under some legal incapacity; and

(e) Where the property in question changes hands, provision is made for the second or subsequent owner to 'inherit' the first owner's right of action and, where the defect was not discoverable before the property changed hands, the three-year limitation period will run from the date on which the subsequent owner discovered or could have discovered it, but subject to the same 'long-stop' period as would have applied to the first owner.

Advantages and disadvantages of the 1986 Act

While it is too early as yet to be sure what the longer-term effects of the Act will be, it should certainly bring some relief to those who, under the old law, would have lost their right to commence an action before it was possible to know that a defect existed. On the other hand, potential defendants now have a reasonable measure of assurance that they will not be faced with heavy actions for negligence long after the facts on which it is based have been forgotten. There is also the advantage that a halt has been called to the recent ebb and flow of Judge-made law on liability for latent damage, at least for the foreseeable future.

One of the first requirements of good law is that, so far as possible, its results should be certain, in the sense that a person should be able to predict the likely extent of any liability which may flow from a particular course of action.

While the concept of a 'long-stop' period is undoubtedly sound (and leaving aside the length of the period which, at fifteen years, was clearly a compromise on the Committee's part) it is useful only if it allows a potential defendant to ascertain the date upon which liability will come to an end. This should then improve his chances of obtaining adequate insurance cover which, if available, will have the advantage not only of protecting the defendant but of ensuring that reasonably adequate funds will be available to remedy any defect if and when it appears during the period of liability — which is clearly in the best interest of the potential plaintiff as well. But (leaving aside the matter of contribution between co-defendants) it is not enough to have a long-stop period of known length: one must also know when it will start.

Unfortunately, at least in construction cases, a given item of damage could be caused by one or more of a number of different breaches of duty. Thus a design error can be a breach of duty, as can the failure of someone checking the design to spot the error. Or a perfectly adequate design may fail through poor workmanship during construction which, in turn, may be overlooked through inadequate supervision. The possibilities are legion, and each possible breach occurs at a different time. Again the new Act applies only to actions in negligence. Thus, at least in theory, a plaintiff can circumvent the 'long-stop' period by bringing his action in contract or under statute.

A further problem with the new Act is peculiar to the construction industry. As stated above, the 'long-stop' period is not to apply where there has been fraud, mistake or deliberate concealment of material facts. There can be no objection to the loss of protection where the defendant has acted fraudulently but the provision on deliberate concealment is another matter. As enacted, it is 'borrowed' directly from the Limitation Act 1980, where it applies principally to actions for personal injury.

The problem for the construction industry is that almost every operation in a construction project necessarily involves some degree of deliberate concealment; foundations conceal sub-soil, pouring concrete conceals reinforcement, brickwork is concealed by plaster — the examples are infinite. While there is some reason to hope that the Courts will in practice take a reasonable view of such situations, there is nothing in the Act itself which compels them to do so.

It is as yet too early to see what the Courts will make of the new legislation.

Appendix E. **Engineers and auditors**

THE INSTITUTION OF CIVIL ENGINEERS
THE CHARTERED INSTITUTE OF PUBLIC
FINANCE AND ACCOUNTANCY

Joint Statement

Engineers and Auditors

The following statement aims to highlight the relationship which exists, in the contract process, between auditors and engineers without detracting from their independence. The growing confusion between the respective roles of auditors and engineers, which has prompted this statement, is born mainly out of inexperience and a mutual ignorance of each other's terms of reference.

The working party which drafted the statement consisted of three senior members of the Institution, and three senior members of the Chartered Institute of Public Finance & Accountancy. The chairman was a senior member of the Institution.

It is hoped that the sentiments expressed in this joint statement will be taken to heart and that the boundaries and defined responsibilities of the two professions will be respected when working together on the same contract. This can only be to the benefit of each and to the mutual benefit of both the Employer and the Contractor.

GENERAL

1. This statement is made jointly by the Institution of Civil Engineers (ICE) and the Chartered Institute of Public Finance and Accountancy (CIPFA) in order to clarify the respective functions of the Engineer and the Employer's Auditors in the contract process with particular reference to civil engineering con-

101

tracts let by Public Authorities. Both bodies commend this statement to their members as a basis for more effective working relationships between their respective disciplines.

2. An authority's chief finance officer is responsible for the financial affairs of the Employer and for maintaining a current internal audit. This responsibility, which for parts of the public sector is embodied in Statute, includes a requirement to review and test check all the systems for management control involved in the contract expenditure process. It is necessary however to emphasise the contractual status of the Engineer.

Both ICE and CIPFA are agreed that, in undertaking contract audits, nothing must be done that might prejudice the role of the Engineer under the contract. Nevertheless the Auditor has a responsibility to report to the Employer on any matters arising from his audit. It is then a matter for the Employer to decide what action should be taken as a result of his Auditor's report.

AUDIT CONSIDERATIONS
The Nature of Audit
3. Internal audit is an independent appraisal function within an authority for the review of activities as a service to all levels of management. It is a control which measures, evaluates and reports upon the effectiveness of internal controls (financial and other) as a contribution to the efficient use of resources within the authority.

4. It is the responsibility of internal audit to review, appraise and report upon:
(a) The soundness, adequacy and application of internal controls.
(b) The extent to which the authority's assets and interests are accounted for and safeguarded from losses of all kinds arising from:
   (i) fraud and other offences
   (ii) waste, extravagance and inefficient administration, poor value for money and other causes.
(c) The suitability and reliability of financial and other management data developed within the authority.

5. The auditor must not affect the relationship between the Contractor, the Employer and the Engineer as defined in the Contract. The auditor needs to maintain the confidence of all concerned when carrying out his duties; this confidence cannot be achieved by prescription but must be the objective of both the Engineer and the Auditor if an effective working relationship between the disciplines is to be achieved.

Audit Methods
6. A list of those systems relating to the contract process which are likely to be found in an audit plan is given in appended notes. The list

should not be taken as exhaustive and, in particular, it excludes the systems for project appraisal and post completion assessment which are not relevant to this joint statement. It gives an indication of those activities which should be reviewed and test checked by audit.

7. The approach to the audit of systems for management control ('the systems audit') may be summarised as follows:

(a) Ascertaining, recording and agreeing with management and other relevant parties the actual system in operation.

(b) Comparing the system as recorded with:
  (i) the requirements of the Contract Conditions
  (ii) the authority's contract regulations, procedures and instructions.

(c) Identifying and ascertaining the reasons for apparent discrepancies between the system defined in (a) and that prescribed by (b) above.

(d) Testing the conformity of the operation of the system by sampling.

(e) Reporting on the results of the audit and, where appropriate, making recommendations.

8. During the progress of the audit it may be necessary to discuss matters with the Engineer or his Representative. This may involve the auditor visiting the Works but always with the relevant technical officer's consent. In carrying out his duties the auditor must be aware that no attempt should be made to interfere with the independence of the Engineer as this could prejudice the position of the Employer under the Contract.

9. The auditor's prime responsibility is to verify that the systems developed by management are sound and are adhered to. These should, amongst other things, enable the final account to be agreed and a certificate issued by the due date.

The Role of the Engineer

10. The obligations of the two parties to the contract are defined in the Conditions of Contract. Guidance on the functions of the Engineer is given in CCSJC Guidance Note 2A. (Available from the Institution, price £1.30.)

Under the Conditions, the Engineer is named and is the representative of the Employer for the purpose of administration of the Contract. The Employer looks to the Engineer to ensure that the Works are properly constructed in accordance with the Terms of the Contract. The Contractor looks to the Engineer for instructions and certification of monies properly due to him.

11. The functions of the Employer, Contractor and Engineer under the Contract are an essential means for ensuring that the Contract is properly executed and justly administered in the interests of both

Employer and Contractor and nothing should be allowed to render these roles less distinct. For example, the Contractor must not take instructions and directions, on matters under the Contract, other than from the Engineer or from the Engineer's Representative.

12. While the Engineer's pre-contract role is usually confined to that of his employer's professional adviser, once the Contract has come into existence by the acceptance of a preferred tender, the Engineer immediately assumes additional and quite separate functions. This new role is fundamentally different from that of an adviser in that he is required to administer the Contract independently of both parties. At the same time the Engineer's duties as his employer's professional adviser continue in parallel with this new role, save that where he is required to act impartially, his responsibilities under the Contract take precedence over his duties as an adviser.

In Conclusion

13. Both bodies believe that if the principles discussed in this statement are implemented, benefits will accrue to all persons involved with the Contract. Problems which would otherwise be raised by audit after the final account is submitted will have been resolved at the time they become apparent and difficulties occasioned by lapse of time and changes of staff will be overcome. The crux of effective joint working is a clear understanding of the differing functions of auditors and engineers and the mutual confidence which can arise from cooperation rather than competition.

SYSTEMS AND PROCEDURES

CONTRACT AUDIT

The following is a list of the systems and procedures likely to be found in an audit plan for examination and test checking. It is not necessarily exhaustive.

Pre Contract Stage

(a) The system for admitting contractors to the approved list and for reviewing their performance and current viability;

(b) The methods for the selection of contractors invited to tender;

(c) The system for regulating the tendering procedure and the letting of contracts;

(d) The system for reviewing the suitability of conditions of contract and tender documents;

(e) Insurance, liquidated damages, and bonding procedures.

Currency of Contract

(a) The system and documentation for providing financial information to ensure adequate management control of the

Authority's capital programme.

(b) The system of on-site control which regulates valuations of work for interim payments;

(c) The system for the examination and control of price fluctuations;

(d) The system for the control and issue of variations;

(e) The system for the receipt and evaluation of contractual claims;

(f) The system for dealing with liquidations.

Post Practical Completion

(a) The system for ensuring that when the final account is produced it is complete and accurate;

(b) The system to ensure that liquidated damages have been recovered where appropriate.

(Further amplification of the audit approach to the above systems is given in *'Contract Audit Guidance Notes'* published by CIPFA in March, 1983.)

Appendix F. **Further reading**

Faster building for industry, National Economic Development Office, London, 1983.

Morrison M.C., *The management of contracts*, undated, Asset Management Group, British Institute of Management, Corby.

Guidelines for the management of major projects in the process industries, National Economic Development Office, London, 1982.

Target cost contracts — a worthwhile alternative, National Economic Development Office, London, 1982.

Jones G.P., *A new approach to the ICE conditions of contract*, Construction Press, 1975.

Marsh P.D.V., *Contract negotiation handbook*, 2nd edition, Gower Press, Aldershot, 1984.

Neale R.H. and D.E., *Construction planning*, Engineering Management Guide, Thomas Telford Ltd, London (in preparation).

Martin A.S. and Grover F.R., *Managing people*, Engineering Management Guide, Thomas Telford Ltd, London, 1988.

Wearne S.H. *et al*, *Control of engineering projects*, 2nd ed., Thomas Telford Ltd, London (in preparation).

Clarke R.H., *Site supervision*, 2nd ed., Thomas Telford Ltd, London, 1988.

Coordinated project information for building works, Committee for Coordinated Project Information (RIBA, RICS, BEC and ACE), 1987.

Appendix G. **Addresses**

ACE	Association of Consulting Engineers 12 Caxton Street London SW1H 0QL	Tel: 01-222 6557
BPF	British Property Federation 35 Catherine Place London SW1E 6DY	Tel: 01-828 0111
CIRIA	Construction Industry Research and Information Association 6 Storeys Gate London SW1	Tel: 01-222 8891
FCEC	Federation of Civil Engineering Contractors 6 Portugal Street London WC2A 2HH (and in other major cities)	Tel: 01-404 4020
FIDIC	Fédération Internationale des Ingénieurs-Conseils PO Box 86 CH-1000 Lausanne 12-Chailly Switzerland	Telex: CH 24698
ICE	Institution of Civil Engineers Great George Street London SW1P 3AA	Tel: 01-222 7722 Fax: 01-222 7500 Telex: 935637
NEDO	National Economic Development Office Millbank Tower London SW1P 4QX	Tel: 01-211 3000 Fax: 01-821 1099 Telex: 945059

PSA	Property Services Agency St. Christopher House Southwark Street London SE1 0TE	Tel: 01-686 5622
RIBA	Royal Institute of British Architects 66 Portland Place London W1	Tel: 01-580 5533
	RIBA Publications Ltd Finsbury Mission 33 Moreland Street London EC1V 8BB	Tel: 01-251 0791
RICS	Royal Institute of Chartered Surveyors 12 Great George Street London SW1P 3AD	Tel: 01-222 7000
TTL	Thomas Telford Ltd (bookshop at the ICE) 1 Heron Quay London E14 9XF	Tel: 01-987 6999 Fax: 01-538 5746 Telex: 298105